THE TECHNIQUE
of the
TELEVISION CAMERAMAN

THE LIBRARY
OF COMMUNICATION TECHNIQUES

THE TECHNIQUE OF THE

TELEVISION CAMERAMAN

by

PETER JONES

with a preface by

J. A. YOUNGMAN

revised by

EDWARD THOMAS

Focal Press Limited · London

Focal Press Inc · New York

ISBN 0 240 50627 8

Illustrations by Dorothy E. Dawe

First published 1965
Second edition 1969
Third edition 1972
Fourth Impression 1972
Fifth Impression 1974
Sixth Impression 1979
Seventh Impression 1980

Spanish edition:
LA TECHNICA DEL CAMARA DE TELEVISION
Instituto Oficial de Radiofusión y Televisión

FOCAL PRESS LTD.,
31 Fitzroy Square, London, W1P 6BH

FOCAL PRESS INC.,
10 East 40th Street, New York, NY 10016

Associated companies:
Pitman Publishing Pty Ltd., Melbourne.
Pitman Publishing New Zealand Ltd., Wellington.

Reproduced and printed by photolithography and bound in Great Britain by A. Wheaton & Co. Ltd., Exeter

CONTENTS

7

FOREWORD

This book marks a step forward in the history of Television literature. It is not difficult to find good reasons for recommending it.

First, it should be said that the book lives up to the promise of its title. It really does teach the reader about the techniques of operating a television camera. You may be reading this preface because you are considering the possibility of becoming a television cameraman. In this book you will find, in full measure, the information you are seeking. If you work in television already, and you are not a cameraman, this book will answer all your questions about his job. And, lastly, if you are a cameraman in training, this book cannot fail to help you.

Except in the fields of engineering and electronics, there are very few books about television so that the addition of one more is an event. And from those engaged in the practical business of putting on television in the studio, the number of books can almost be counted on one hand. Furthermore, such books as there are have so far covered very wide fields, dealing with directing, planning, lighting, sound, make-up, composition and much more in one volume. This book is almost unique in that it concentrates on one aspect of television production only, and that in great detail. It could well inspire other specialists to add their own contributions to the available literature.

The author shows great skill in keeping to his own subject and yet at the same time he does not ignore the value of teamwork during a television production. He does not waste our time with the more extravagant and exotic uses of the television camera for he knows that camera tricks have a value only if used rarely.

When Peter Jones wrote the book he was a practising cameraman. Herein lies its greatest value. All too often books are written after the authors have moved on from a particular job, perhaps because only promotion or retirement provide the time and opportunity to write. Excellent though many such books are, they frequently approach the subject matter with detachment, without sympathy to those trying to learn.

But Peter Jones is helpful and practical; he is sympathetic to the difficulties of the aspiring cameraman: he has not forgotten what it was like when he struggled with the problems he discusses. One can feel throughout a warmth and a genuine desire to help the beginner.

The book is both thoughtful and thought provoking, and this latter quality alone should commend it also to the older hands amongst the television camera fraternity.

This volume can be read, like a novel, at one sitting, since it is eminently readable. This over, it should not be placed in the book-shelf and forgotten; it should be read again, in sections, and digested. Indeed it could well be taken, step by step, and worked through as a training manual in all studios where time is available for such activities.

This book can scarcely fail to improve the standard of television camerawork wherever it is read, and studied; and that, I hope, will be throughout the world.

J. A. Youngman.

Former Instructor, Television.
BBC Staff Training Department

INTRODUCTION

As the title suggests, this book deals with the technique of television camerawork. There can be no doubt now that this technique is specialized—that is, peculiar to the television industry—since the operational problems cannot be compared with those in the film world. They are not more difficult: they are different.

Exactly how the cameraman is trained varies between organizations. He may have the opportunity for systematic training and experience, with introductions to other operational jobs. Or he may receive only hurried and incomplete tuition.

Other senior cameramen have agreed with me that there is a need for a manual devoted to the technique of the television cameraman, to which they could refer newcomers to the profession. This book has been written in an attempt to answer that need.

It has been my aim throughout to concentrate on the techniques that are regarded as standard practice in the television industry—certainly in British television. I have taken great pains to avoid imposing my own particular methods on the reader. Where my views might differ from recognized procedure, I have said so.

But these cases are rare. There is a refreshing uniformity in what is considered good camerawork. An experienced cameraman can study a television picture emanating from anywhere in the world and know whether the cameraman responsible is a competent operator or not. And the yardstick for this estimation is the technique employed. But good technique does more than merely satisfy the professional curiosity of other cameramen: it has a direct bearing on the quality of a television programme.

The absence of good technique can detract from the appeal of a programme as effectively as a badly contrived script or an incompetent artist. Its presence can raise the value of a good programme to the standard of a classic. It cannot, however, rescue an indifferent show from the final judgment of the "off" switch on the viewer's receiver.

Since there are many books on the market dealing with the technical side of television, this book concentrates entirely on technique. No attempt is made to explain the electronic function of the television camera. Technical subjects have been treated from the point of view of basic principles only. There is no inventory here of all the equipment in current use.

What the trainee to the profession really wants to know—and only needs to know—is how he can become a good cameraman. This entails learning the flexibility and limitations of his equipment; the difference between a "good shot" and a "bad shot"; the correct technique to be employed when executing camera movement; and the recognized methods of overcoming problems.

These are the subjects around which this book has been written. But the advice contained in the following pages—useful as it was to me in my early days—must be joined with practical experience on the studio floor. I have repeatedly emphasized throughout the book that the cameraman must practise at every opportunity if he is to master the technique of camerawork.

Read the book by all means—I hope you do—but never forget that "knowing how" is inferior to "can do"!

I have deliberately refrained from dealing specifically with the techniques of colour television camerawork. The reason for this is that most of these techniques are virtually identical to those employed in monochrome television. There *are* differences, of course, and some of these have been briefly mentioned in the text, but the main responsibility does not lie with the cameraman. The colour camera is invariably equipped with a viewfinder which shows a monochrome picture and the cameraman is in no position to adjust his composition to the requirements of colour.

No one can write a book of this nature without the help of friends. Of these I have had more than my rightful share, and it would be impossible to attempt to mention them all here. I hope they will accept a communal "Thank you" from me.

But I must record my special appreciation to the following: Miss Dorothy Dawe for her excellent illustrations, which are so essential to a work of this nature; Mr. J. A. Youngman for gallantly vetting the finished manuscript, and for his excellent advice and suggestions; Mr. Walter Hazlehurst for his invaluable help with the chapter on "Television Lighting"; Mr. Terence de Lacey for permission to use an extract from his play *Night Train To Nowhere*; T.W.W. Ltd., for permission to reproduce floor-plans; Miss Glenda Bell, for her help with my rough notes and for typing the final manuscript; and my wife for her willing interest and assistance.

1

THE CAMERAMAN'S QUALITIES

THE television cameraman is in the front line of television operations. He operates what might appear to be the most important piece of equipment of a visual medium. His work appears interesting and sometimes exciting to the lay public, which knows nothing and cares less about the dozens of vitally important people behind the scenes who all contribute their various skills to the success of the production. It is little wonder, therefore, that the job of the television cameraman has acquired a certain aura—a glamour perhaps—among the various operational jobs in the studio production team.

The glamorous nature of camerawork meant that almost every newcomer to the operational side of television wanted to be a cameraman. Even today, the number of applicants for the post of trainee cameraman is usually more than double the number applying for a position in the sound department, for example.

Unfortunately, there has been a lot of nonsense written about the television cameraman, even by people within the industry. Some of the articles which have dealt with the qualities a man must have in order to become a television cameraman have been a little over-enthusiastic, to say the least. Some of the remarks have given more embarrassment to cameramen than advice to would-be applicants.

A fair indication of the worth of a job is the opinion of those who have spent some time in it. Probably ninety-nine out of a hundred television cameramen would admit that they would do nothing else. When the time comes to leave camerawork to progress within the industry, very few go without a feeling of regret, however attractive or necessary the step-up they are taking. And in later years they will invariably speak with affection of their period as a cameraman.

Yes! There is something about the job. It is interesting, varied, immensely satisfying, and very often exciting. It is also highly skilled, and jolly hard work.

What are the qualities a trainee cameraman should possess if he is to make a success of his career?

Keenness

In the first place he must be keen—and not only while he is learning his job, and participating in the make-up of television programmes. It must be a stronger feeling than that. There will be times when he will feel that he has done it all before and that his job has become a routine. That is when his standards will fall, together with his worth and reputation.

This keenness must be more than excitement at the glamorous prospects. It must continue through the early days of comparative drudgery: clearing the cables from the path of moving cameras, attending to monitors, and so on.

It must persist throughout his training as a tracker (who guides, perhaps driving, the camera mounting), which he must learn to do well. Most good cameramen have been good trackers.

The cameraman must continue to be keen throughout the time when he is learning camera technique, and while he is waiting for his chance to put his knowledge into practice. And it must still be there when he is experienced—at the top of his profession perhaps—when there seems to be no further challenge to his skill, or when the programmes he is working on seem monotonous and repetitious.

Keenness must never leave him. There are many excellent cameramen waiting to take the place of "old Joe who used to be good but is getting a bit past it these days". It is a wonderful job: but even the best of cameramen sometimes forget this. His first chance to reveal his mettle will probably be semi-static shots on a small show. Then it's up to him.

Youth

Secondly, he should be young. As a general rule 25 should be regarded as the maximum age limit for applicants. On the other hand the job requires a certain amount of maturity, and trainees under the age of 19 or 20 are not entirely suitable. These are rough guides (and there are many instances of their being successfully disregarded) but it seems to be a fact that the 20–25 age group provides the best source of trainee material.

There are good reasons for this emphasis on youth. The trainee has much to learn, and it will take him many years to acquire this knowledge. His greatest asset in later years will be the practical experience he has acquired of all types of camerawork, and this, too, takes time. The tree he intends to climb can be a high one, and he may be well into his thirties before he attains the rank of senior cameraman. But most important of all, his career as a cameraman in busy network studios may well end by the time he is 40.

Television camerawork is a young man's job. Although there are experienced cameramen who are well into their forties, and even fifties, it must be said that they really are living on borrowed time. Around middle age, keenness invariably becomes a little blunted; reactions become slower; the eyes a little tired; and the physical effort involved more and more arduous as the months go by.

Much depends, of course, on the physical and mental state of the individual. Just as important is the complexity and speed of programme the cameraman is expected to work on, and the type of equipment he is using. Some of the smaller studios, where programme technique is simple and the pace relatively slow, do not create the conditions which can overtax the older cameraman.

But the big studio—high-geared, working at the normal furious pace, with television plays and major musical shows occurring day after day—needs the backing of young, fit, keen and skilled cameramen. It is a sad thought, but there is no room here for the cameraman who takes that second or two longer than anyone else to move from one set to another. There is little sympathy for the operator who forgets his next shot, or who finds difficulty in holding focus on moving shots. It is a young man's job, and it is advisable to start young.

Physical Condition

Physical disabilities are obviously a severe drawback to success in this career. Some of the cameraman's duties involve much physical effort—particularly on outside broadcasts—and any physical deficiency becomes a weak link in an otherwise strong chain. Carrying gear, heaving cables, pushing dollies, can be wearying work.

Contrary to many people's opinion, the wearing of spectacles is no drawback to the aspiring cameraman. Quite a number of top cameramen wear them, and they are no more of a nuisance to the wearer when he is operating a camera, than they are during his normal off-duty hours.

He must have manual co-ordination. This is not the magical quality that some people would have us believe. It simply means

15

that sometimes the cameraman's right hand must be doing things the left hand knows nothing about. The man who can do this is not a superman. But the man who does not possess this aptitude is unlikely to succeed as a cameraman. Although most people manage to coordinate three or four different limb movements simultaneously, this is not a universal ability. Experience improves, but cannot create, dexterity where it does not exist.

Picture Sense

He must have a sense of picture composition. This is something that can be taught to any intelligent trainee, and it is hoped that the relevant chapters later in this book will provide some guidance on this subject. Anyone with average intelligence can learn to compose pleasing and balanced pictures. But, as will be discussed later, the television cameraman must develop an instinct for this art. He will often be called upon to change to another lens, move his camera, focus on a new subject, and compose a new picture, all in the space of a few seconds. These tasks must eventually become instinctive. Manual co-ordination and a feeling for composition provide the ideal combination.

He must have a sympathetic attitude towards the content matter of the shows he is required to work on. He must feel a genuine desire to present whatever subject he is shooting in the most interesting, dramatic, informative, or exciting manner. Unless he feels this sense of participation, he will not be in the best frame of mind to interpret the director's intentions. He should be a little artistic, therefore, and should feel a real sense of pleasure when he is responsible for good, artistic, technically competent camerawork.

It usually follows from this that the best cameramen have a touch of the extrovert about them. Most of them will usually execute a higher standard of camerawork in front of a studio audience, than they will under normal studio conditions. They will not readily admit this; but it is invariably true. There is something of the show-off in every good cameraman; but, above all, he is a professional—and professionalism comes first.

Technical Knowledge

Some prior knowledge of photography or optics is useful to the would-be cameraman, since some of the terms used in his training will then be familiar to him. If he knows something about *f* numbers and focal length of lenses, for example, the task of

16

training him will be a little easier. But such knowledge is by no means essential. In many cases it is far more desirable to start with an open mind, than to have to abandon certain preconceived notions and techniques which might have become habitual.

A knowledge of the TV studio's electronic intricacies—or even an understanding of the workings of the television camera—can remain a closed book to him, and he can still rise to the top of his profession. This might sound like heresy to many cameramen, but there are many others, masters of their craft, who hardly know a volt from an amp.

A basic knowledge of electricity and electronics is an advantage; it would be folly to deny this. Some cameramen can get the best results from their equipment only if they know *why* something happens when they operate a certain control. But, generally speaking, all the cameraman needs to know is *what* happens.

A trainee cameraman will not be wasting his time by any means if he attempts to understand the basic principles of the technical side of his work. Some of this information will be painlessly acquired during his training and subsequent practical experience. But he should not be discouraged from becoming a cameraman if he is not technically minded. It is far more important that he should be artistically minded.

Hard Worker

He must be a glutton for work. His working day will sometimes be as long as twelve hours, and during that time he must give full attention to his job. Television—to use a well-worn but none the less true cliché—requires a high level of teamwork. The cameraman must compromise with other sections, and work harmoniously with them. And it will follow that if he falls short of the standard of work expected of him, the repercussions can be felt in other departments. Many a small mistake by one man has led to a series of errors on the part of others. The net result is often disaster for the programme concerned.

Good Mixer

Finally, he should be a good mixer. His work will bring him into contact with people—lots of them—from all walks of life. It will soon be obvious to the newcomer that he must learn to mix well with other members of his crew, and with the personnel of the other sections in the studio.

But he will also find himself mixing with the people who appear on the shows he is concerned with. Although the bulk of them will almost certainly be from the entertainment world—and the cameraman must learn to understand their difficult way of life and their artistic temperament—he might just as easily rub shoulders with Heads of State, leaders of the Church, or the local refuse collector being interviewed about his pools win.

The cameraman must respect these guests, and do nothing which would cause them to be embarrassed, annoyed, or in any way distracted when they are in the studio.

On no account must he adopt a superior attitude to artists who, because of their ignorance of the workings of television, do apparently silly things, and hamper his work. Most strangers to a television studio are bemused by the complexity of all that is happening around them. Nobody seems to be taking any notice of them, but if they move someone asks them to keep still.

Appearing on television can be very unsettling to all but the experienced, and the cameraman must play his part in making the artists' ordeal as light as possible. He can best do this by getting on with his job and leaving the floor manager to convey to the artists any of the director's instructions. If the cameraman wants an artist repositioned, the instructions should be passed through the floor manager—that is his job.

If the cameraman has to deal directly with artists, however, he should be respectful and patient. But this should not be taken to the point of servile veneration when dealing with such artists as world-famous film stars. Artists of this calibre usually turn out to be very nice people who are very good at their job. They expect the cameraman to behave towards them as one professional to another, and that is how the cameraman should conduct himself—with, perhaps, some added respect for the high standards they have attained in their profession.

Duties and Responsibilities

Quite obviously the cameraman's first duty is to become competent at his job. A director should never be forced to accept inferior camerawork because the cameraman is incapable of performing any recognized aspect of his work. This sounds elementary, but it should always be in the cameraman's mind, not only while he is learning the skills and techniques of his profession, but also when he has had the benefit of some years' experience.

He should never miss the opportunity of operating equipment which is new to him. And anything he can add to his knowledge—either by reading, or talking to other cameramen—will never be wasted. In later years he will often be called upon to advise directors on the suitability of their ideas, or on the value of little-used pieces of equipment. The more he knows about anything connected with his job the better.

Above all he must strive to attain a high standard in the actual technique of camerawork. Tracking, crabbing, focusing, zooming —there is a right and wrong way to do each of them. He must practise until these skills are second nature to him. Having reached that state, he must guard against the danger of allowing his standards to fall.

The director is entitled to assume that the cameraman will compose his pictures correctly, and that camera movement will be performed smoothly, with no loss of focus. Unless the cameraman is master of his craft he will command no respect. Apart from the fact that he will be a weak link, his career will be doomed. A cameraman's reputation has a habit of spreading beyond the four walls of his studio.

It is the cameraman's responsibility to ensure that his equipment is kept in a good working state. The more technical aspects—the electronics, mechanics, optics—are normally maintained by qualified engineers. Panning heads must be constantly checked, and adjusted if necessary. Dollies must be cleaned periodically to keep dust from their moving parts. As described in a later chapter, lenses must be handled and cleaned with care. The various pieces of equipment are the tools of his trade, and the cameraman will be blaming himself if he ever blames his tools for bad workmanship.

During rehearsals and transmissions he must avoid becoming involved in other people's problems. There are many things which can easily be a distraction to the inexperienced cameraman. If something goes amiss with some aspect of another section's work, he must resist the temptation to become involved.

Even if a set collapses at the other end of the studio—and this has happened more than once when a studio is "on the air"—the cameraman must concentrate firmly on his own job, and leave the solving of the problem to those responsible. Remember, a mistake by one person can snowball into disaster if other operators allow themselves to become involved, and momentarily lose concentration.

This advice holds good in many other instances. The cameraman must never move pieces of equipment belonging to other sections, however well meaning his intentions. In particular, all the "properties" around the set—the books, ornaments and sundry objects—must be left severely alone. If a bottle of ink has tipped and spread its contents over a white table cloth, the cameraman must assume that it is intended to be like that. He will receive no thanks for putting matters to right. He must touch nothing and concentrate on his job, whatever the temptation to do otherwise.

When he has had a number of years' experience his instinct will tell him when he can safely allow himself to become involved in other matters, but until then he should mind his own business.

However, this attitude should not be carried to the point of ignoring the technical and artistic problems of other sections. He must work in harmony with them, and the more the cameraman can glean about the work of other departments the better.

In particular he should try to appreciate the special difficulties of the boom operator, and adopt a sympathetic attitude to his attempts to place the microphone as close to artists as is necessary.

The cameraman must remember to perform all camera movements and lens changes as quietly as possible. Some noise is inevitable, but it must be kept to a minimum.

Above all, the cameraman must remember that it is his duty to give the director what he wants. He can do this only if he has acquired a knowledge and skill of a high level, and he should constantly strive to reach and maintain this required standard.

2

THE TELEVISION STUDIO

WHEN a trainee cameraman enters a television studio for the first time, he can be excused if he feels rather bemused by the complexity of everything he sees. There appears to be very little coherence in the activity going on around him. And every available space seems to be occupied by scenery, unfamiliar pieces of equipment, artists, or studio operators.

The language, too, is different. Strange terms are bandied about, which everyone but the newcomer understands. He finds that he is continually in the way—an apparent nuisance. The pace of the activity around him changes from static to frantic in a matter of seconds, and with little warning.

But when he has recovered from the initial shock and can see things a little more clearly, he begins to understand the individual functions of the various departments. He realizes, too, that what he thought was semi-organized chaos is, in fact, a highly professional intermingling of a variety of skills. And if he looks closer still, he will detect a camaraderie between studio personnel which will be one of the many rewarding features of his future, professional life.

That is not to say that cameramen do not have their differences with the sound or lighting department, or that tempers do not sometimes get just a little frayed! The pace and tension of television inevitably takes its toll. But such upheavals are minor and temporary: the permanently quarrelsome character is a rarity in television.

Other People's Jobs

What little dissension there is, usually arises out of a lack of understanding of other people's problems. And the newcomer, with so much to learn about his own job before he can become a useful member of the team, might never come to appreciate fully the problems of other sections. Unless a cameraman has tried to operate a sound boom, for example, he can never really understand the difficulties of the job.

In some studios he may have the opportunity to gain some practical experience of other studio jobs. But learning to be an efficient cameraman is a full-time job.

Nevertheless, the cameraman must know something about the work of every department in a television studio. He cannot operate his camera in a cloud of isolation. A knowledge of the special problems of the vision (or video) control operator and the sound boom operator in particular is essential if he is to become a cameraman at all. But he will never be anything but a fairly good cameraman—whatever his personal attributes—if he knows nothing at all about the problems of the many other people who work alongside him.

A brief description of the duties of most of the people engaged in the operational side of television will be of help to the trainee cameraman. There are whole books devoted to many of the sections we shall discuss here—television directing, make-up, lighting, designing, and so on—and we can only scratch the surface of each subject in the space of a few paragraphs.

Nevertheless, it is hoped that the information will make the cameraman realize that he is merely a cog in a large wheel. Perhaps it will help him to think of others, despite his own difficulties. And it might arouse his curiosity, and make him keen to know more about the work of other sections. If it does, not only will this chapter have been worthwhile in itself, but the trainee will have taken one of the bigger steps towards being something more than just a good cameraman.

Since the trainee cameraman will spend his working life "on the studio floor", we can study first the people who will work alongside him. And we shall look at their duties in relation to his own.

The Boom Operator

We have already mentioned the boom operator. He is responsible for placing his microphone in the best positions to pick up the sound which originates from the studio floor.

In most cases this means the voices of artists. And since artists turn their heads, move around, and vary the intensity of the sound they make, the boom operator must be able to alter the position of his microphone at will. And the piece of equipment he uses to achieve this is usually called a sound boom.

This normally takes the form of a three-wheeled platform—which can be raised to a height of about 5 ft—on which the operator stands. Mounted on this platform, and about level with his waist, is a telescopic, metal arm, at the end of which is mounted the microphone itself. By operating certain controls which are connected to a system of strings and pulleys, the operator can extend and retract the arm, turn and tilt the microphone through an extensive range, and—since the arm pivots freely about its mounting—raise, lower, or swing it from side to side at will.

The boom operator has a skilled, arduous, and often quite uncomfortable job. Guided by the sound balancer (sound mixer), he has instinctively to estimate the optimum microphone position. He can seldom use a picture monitor to help his judgment or to see whether he is in shot.

He must be conversant with the polar diagram of each microphone he uses, i.e. its relative sensitivity to sound in various directions. Some microphones have an omnidirectional response (equal in all directions). Others pick up sound from a limited area only at the front of the microphone, and these are the types normally attached to a boom.

He needs to know the form and direction that sound waves take when they originate from a variety of sources, and where he should place his microphone in order to receive maximum quality sound from them.

But that is not the end of his task. He must endeavour to achieve these ideals without allowing his microphone to be seen in the cameramen's shots. And since these shots will change continuously from close-ups to wide shots, and are often accompanied by movement of the artists or cameras, he must be very alert indeed.

The boom operator should have a general idea of typical camera treatment and shot sizes. Where turret lenses are fitted, a quick glance to see which lens is in use will give him an immediate clue (for the camera distance) to the resultant image size. He cannot, of course, estimate in this way with the zoom lens.

Finally, he must manoeuvre the arm of the boom, and the microphone, in such a way that the shadows which they cast will never be seen in any of the cameramen's shots. This is one of the more difficult aspects of the boom operator's work, since a great number of powerful lights are normally directed at a set from a variety of angles. And this set will probably be shot from a number of camera positions.

The difficulties of the boom operator impose limitations on the cameraman. Conversely, many of the boom operator's problems arise from the very nature of camerawork. That is why close liaison between the cameraman and the boom operator is so essential.

Cameramen can help the sound department by never forgetting that sound on a television programme is as important as the picture. There are many occasions when cameramen must restrain their artistic desires to accommodate sound requirements. Equally, the sound department must occasionally accept what they might regard as inferior sound when the picture content is more important.

But the cameraman can best help by maintaining uniformity in the framing of his shots. Every close-up must be consistent, for example, and the shots the cameraman finalizes during rehearsals must be the same as those he offers during transmission.

As we shall discuss in later chapters, the cameraman should mark the position of his dolly during rehearsals as he finalizes his shots. The boom operator, or his trackers, will probably do the same for each new position of the boom.

If the cameraman is careless during transmission and does not place his dolly on the correct marks, he might easily occupy the next marked position for the boom. We have already said that the studio floor can be a very crowded place, and pieces of equipment often have to be moved within inches of each other. The cameraman would probably be the first to complain if a badly sited boom prevented him from taking his rehearsed shots.

Any camera movement, lens changes, or manipulations of the dollies must be carried out with the minimum of noise. A breathless love-scene which is accompanied by a series of metallic bangs and squeaks will hardly be a dramatic success. Yet how often have we experienced this while watching television in our own homes!

And most of the blame must lie with the cameramen. Some noise is inevitable, since it is impossible to move heavy equipment noiselessly around a studio. But the cameraman must never become careless because he is in a hurry. Careful movements and timing are essential. Microphones are very sensitive pieces of apparatus.

The boom operator is the member of the sound department whose work is directly interrelated with that of the cameraman. The remainder of the operators in this section are normally employed in the sound control room.

Here the sound balancer adjusts and blends the relative strengths of his sound sources, using a series of faders. Here, too, are the

24

facilities for supplying music and sound-effects by means of discs and tapes.

Although the work carried out by the personnel in the sound control room is important and highly skilled, we shall not discuss it any further here since we are concerning ourselves mainly with those duties which directly affect camerawork.

The Floor Manager

The director's contact-man on the studio floor is usually known as the floor manager, or studio manager—sometimes as the Production Assistant (PA). He may be assisted by a stage manager, or assistant floor manager (AFM) who repositions props and furniture, etc.

Basically, he is the link between the director and everyone on the studio floor who is not wearing headphones. Cameramen, boom operators, trackers, and the floor manager himself all wear headphones, through which they receive the director's instructions. But such people as stage-hands, electricians, musicians and—in particular—artists, rely on the floor manager to relay any instructions from the director to them.

The floor manager can be regarded as the man who is in charge on the studio floor. Although his authority over the technical operators is not absolute, productional activities on the studio floor are under his control from the time that the rehearsals commence. He is responsible for the smooth-running of the studio during rehearsals and transmissions, and a good floor manager can prevent literally hours from being wasted during a day's work.

He is mainly concerned, however, with controlling the artists in a programme, and because of this he must be a man who combines tact with authority and sympathy with firmness.

He is at the director's beck and call, and he must be constantly alert. Rehearsals are his busiest time. Then he must continuously relay instructions to artists, moving them when necessary and marking on the floor any of their positions which are important. The position of every piece of furniture, and many of the props., once finalized, must also be marked to ensure they are in the same place for transmission.

He must also direct and supervise the work of the stage-hands, particularly when scenery or set-dressings must be moved. And he must establish a means of indicating to artists when they must speak, move, speed up, slow down, and many other eventualities.

There is a fairly universal system of signals which floor managers employ in these circumstances.

We have mentioned only some of his duties. These are so varied that on many large shows the floor manager is usually allocated two or three assistants to help him carry out all his tasks.

The cameraman can best help the floor manager by concentrating on his camerawork and not interfering with things that do not concern him. In particular, he must relay any comments or instructions to artists through the floor manager. And he must never move any furniture or set-dressings to help his composition. These should be moved by the people who are responsible for them, and then always under the floor manager's supervision.

The Stage-Hands

They are responsible for erecting sets in a studio, and arranging such items as furniture and heavy props. In fact, their work is manual in character though it must be intelligently applied.

When erecting sets, for example, the position of everything they contain must correspond to a drawing of the set, superimposed on a floor-plan of the studio, and prepared by the designer. If the stage-hands are careless when erecting their sets they can be responsible for much confusion and wasted rehearsal time. The lighting director, for example, arranges his lighting rig in conjunction with the floor-plan. If the sets are incorrectly sited, they will not be lit as planned. Either the sets or the lights must be repositioned, and this adds up to wasted rehearsal time.

Much of the stage-hands' work involves moving heavy and cumbersome items, often when the studio is "on the air". They must learn to carry out these tasks quickly and quietly, and some stage crews attain a remarkable degree of skill and speed.

Since they are also responsible for placing caption-boards in front of cameras, the cameraman can help by letting them know where and when he wants his caption-boards—and then sticking to this. And he should experiment with different camera positions before requesting that major pieces of scenery should be moved to improve the composition of his shots.

Property buyers are responsible for acquiring the various bits and pieces which are added to a scene to give it authenticity. These items are normally referred to as props., and it would be impossible to give a complete list of articles that are regarded as props. Broadly speaking anything added to a bare set comes under this category, having been chosen by the designer as part of his treatment.

The people who assemble and dress the sets with these props, guided by the set designer, do not really come under the designation of stage-hands. But the two sections work in such close collaboration that they have been mentioned here.

It cannot be emphasized too strongly that cameramen must leave props. strictly alone. Many articles used in a television programme are valuable, and have often been borrowed or hired for the day, sometimes at great cost. They must not be touched, then, and they should only be moved on the director's instructions and under the floor manager's supervision.

Electricians, carpenters, mechanical engineers, and so on are found on the studio floor from time to time, but important though their work is it does not normally concern the cameraman directly, so we need not consider it here.

We can now go behind the scenes a little, and look at the people the public rarely sees, but who are as important as those in the front line of television operations.

The Vision Control Operator

As its name suggests, "vision control" is the link in the picture chain, where the quality of the studio pictures is controlled. Here is the technical processing point, where the tonal quality and exposure of each cameraman's picture are continually adjusted; where the pictorial effects of camera outputs are matched, to blend unobtrusively with the rest of the contributory picture sources (slides, film, etc.).

The television camera is attached to its camera control unit (CCU) by its "umbilical cord" a long multi-core cable plugged to a nearby studio wall-point. The electrical supplies and waveforms required by the camera are fed along the camera cable from the CCU, while the return picture signal (video) is amplified and processed in the CCU, before being passed on to the vision mixer, ready for selection by the production director.

The studio cameras' group of CCUs may be housed in a room adjacent to the studio, or in a distant central apparatus room serving several studios.

By adjusting circuits in each camera's CCU, we can modify the picture quality. This control was once done by operational video engineers seated beside each unit. These specialists were also responsible for the electronic maintenance of the equipment.

Later, one man became able to control two cameras' units simultaneously, and this arrangement is still in use—especially on mobile television units.

Nowadays larger television networks have often adopted a more sophisticated set-up. The various CCU controls are adjusted remotely, from a communal vision control desk adjacent to the lighting control console. Here a single vision control operator, or video engineer, continually adjusts the picture tonal quality and brightness of all picture sources for optimum effect, in conjunction with the lighting director's treatment.

The VC operator's job requires a peculiar combination of electronic knowledge, technical skill, dexterity, and artistic sensitivity. He must be quick to spot the first signs of technical defects; able to apply instant but subtle corrections to improve the picture.

There may be a number of video adjustments for each camera, but the main functions are usually combined in one ingenious master control. This is in the form of a mushroom-shaped knob. Tilted forwards and backwards, it alters the camera's lens aperture —an exposure control covering ± 1 stop perhaps. Rotating the control knob causes the "sit" of the picture (its "black level") to change. This "sit" adjustment moves the entire range of picture tones up or down the tonal scale. The principle effect of "sitting down" is to cause the scene's darkest tones to merge to black; while "sitting up" will grey them out.

Finally, by pressing the knob, the VC operator can make an instant comparison on the same monitor, between his newly-adjusted picture, and that already "on the air".

In a colour system, a further group of controls enables him to adjust the overall colour quality of the picture.

And so we see that, to draw a crude parallel with the world of photography, the cameraman frames and focuses the image, while the VC operator exposes and "processes" the resultant picture. Together they combine to interpret the pictorial aims of the scenic designer and the lighting director, who, in their turn interpret the director's intentions.

Let us imagine that the VC operator has set his controls to present a properly exposed, artistically pleasing picture of an artist, who is standing in a fairly dark set. It will be a low-key shot, with perhaps the brightest portions being such small areas as the artist's face and hands.

If the cameraman then changes his shot to a close-up of the

artist's face, the VC operator is presented with an entirely different exposure problem. The face, as we have said, is the brightest part of the original shot. And now this bright area almost completely fills the screen. The subjective brightness of the picture has changed.

If the VC operator leaves his controls set for the long shot, this close-up will not appear to be correctly exposed, because tonal proportions have altered. The VC operator must adjust the necessary controls immediately this new shot is offered, and he must continue to make these electronic corrections for every new shot the cameraman takes.

This need for matching is very important, though it is not always appreciated by the layman until it is badly done. Careless matching of pictures can be distracting to the viewer.

How often have we seen an artist who appears to be wearing a light-grey suit in one shot and a black suit in the next? How many times have we seen an artist suddenly acquire a deep suntan when shot from another angle?

These occurrences are invariably the fault of indifferent matching of shots, provided that the shots have been correctly lit, and have been taken from within the lighting director's limits by the cameramen—and providing shots are as rehearsed.

The adjustments which the VC operator must make for each new shot take time. And matching increases the interval between the time the cameraman frames his shot, and the moment when it can be used by the director. Nevertheless, top-class operators can accomplish these tasks in a couple of seconds—but they need the cameraman's assistance if they are to do so.

The cameraman must always frame and focus his next shot as soon as he possibly can. It does not matter that this new shot might not be needed for another thirty seconds. He must show it immediately to the VC operator, who can make his adjustments and attend to matching.

Having offered the shot, the cameraman must hold it steady until he can see that it has been finally adjusted to the VC operator's satisfaction. If the shot is not needed for a while, there might be an opportunity to check the camera channel; to correct a fault, to put just that edge on its performance.

The cameraman must not delay the lining up of each new shot, then. And during rehearsals he must resist the temptation to frame shots which he is not expected to take in the programme. The VC operator might be unaware that the cameraman is merely enjoying himself, and he might spend a busy afternoon exposing shots that no one wants.

Excess light can easily damage the camera-tube; whether by shooting straight into lamps, over-bright practicals, or strong specular reflections from shiny surfaces. Where possible the VC operator will stop the lens down fully, to try to reduce the risk of "burn in", but the cameraman should avoid such problems as far as possible. Similarly, he must avoid pointing his camera into lights accidentally, when distracted (e.g., with his crib card), or when moving about the studio.

Most cameras have a device incorporated in them which covers the front of the camera tube when it is not in use. This protects the sensitive tube from bright lights, for example, when the channel is not manned. It must never be removed by the cameraman without the VC operator's permission. And it must be replaced whenever the camera is left unattended for more than about five minutes.

Cameramen must remember that they merely operate an expensive and complicated piece of equipment. A moment's thoughtlessness can all too easily lead to damage that others have to rectify.

The Lighting Director

His duties are examined more closely in the chapter dealing with television lighting, so we need mention him only briefly here.

He is responsible for devising and directing the production lighting treatment; for creating mood and environmental illusion with light, while satisfying the technical limitations of the television system. He will determine the lighting techniques, the lenses' apertures.

He may be the person ultimately responsible for the studio's picture quality; the technical manager in charge of the operational crew. The VC operator and the lighting console operator coordinate their work under his direction.

We come now to the nerve-centre of the television studio—the production control room. This is where the director sits with his assistants, together with the vision-mixer (technical director in the US). It is here that the programme is co-ordinated and sent out to the viewer.

The Director

He is the man who is responsible for transforming a television script into a television programme. In some cases (nearly always in the US) a separate producer will conceive the idea for the programme, assemble the content matter, contact the artists, and so on. The director will then concentrate on the technical problems of making the programme possible in terms of television.

Sometimes directors combine the duties of the producer with their own—the practice varies from studio to studio and programme to programme. But once the show has reached the studio floor, the director is in charge. He must control the operators of the various sections to produce the sort of programme he has envisaged.

He must understand the limitations and scope of all the facilities of a television studio, and he must know how and when to use them in order to create the effect he is seeking.

When planning his show he must take into consideration the problems of the cameramen, sound operators, lighting directors, VC operators, stage-hands, and so on. He must know how long it will take an experienced crew to put up a new set during transmission, for example, or whether he can expect a cameraman to move from one set to another in so many seconds.

When planning his shots and camera positions, he must not forget that the boom must be allowed for, and he cannot script a very wide shot and expect to get intimate sound at the same time.

These are very obvious examples, of course, and the last one quoted would hardly ever occur in practice. But they illustrate some of the points that the director must consider in the early stages of a programme.

Once rehearsals are under way he must be capable of conveying his ideas to the studio operators. He must combine all the various skills he has at his disposal in a competent and artistic manner.

To help him do this he is normally provided with a bank of eight or more monitors, on which he can see the pictures from each source he will use in his programme.

One monitor will show the pictures that Camera One is offering, another will show Camera Two's pictures and so on. Film and outside sources will appear on their respective monitors, and there is often a monitor provided on which the director can preview certain composite shots or special effects before he cuts to them.

In addition, there is always a master-monitor on which the director can see the effect of his directing. The pictures he sees there are the pictures the viewer will see when the show is transmitted: it is the studio output monitor. During rehearsals he will use it to shape his programme, studying the effect of his cuts, and pans, etc. During transmissions he should see there the programme he envisaged, and which he rehearsed to achieve.

He must make the final decisions on all operational matters. He can accept or reject a cameraman's shot, order the repositioning of sets and pieces of scenery, direct the artists in the manner of their performances, and pass judgment on the quality of sound.

It is he who decides the order in which shots are to be taken, and when and how the change from one to another will be made. Assuming that the personnel of each section are competent and experienced, he is entirely responsible for the success or otherwise of the programme concerned.

It is the cameraman's duty to interpret the director's intentions, and convert them into professional, artistic television. The duties of the cameraman in this respect are examined more closely in a later chapter. There is no doubt that indifferent camerawork can ruin a well-planned show. The director has a right to expect his cameramen to be competent and sympathetic, and the sooner the trainee reaches that stage the better.

Although top-class cameramen can sometimes help the director to produce a show that is superior to the one he envisaged, he must ultimately receive the credit or the blame for the quality of his programmes.

The Producer's Assistant

She may be called the production secretary or the producer's assistant. Whatever the title given her, she is the director's right-hand woman. In the planning stage of the programme she fulfils the normal duties of a personal secretary—arranging meetings, contacting artists, typing letters and scripts, and so on.

Much of the routine preparatory work is often left entirely in her hands, and she should be intelligent and extremely efficient. During rehearsals and transmissions, however, her duties and responsibilities take an entirely different form. In US television, in fact, these additional duties are the responsibility of the associate director.

She normally sits alongside the director and supplies him with the sort of information he cannot afford to give his time to. She is responsible for keeping an accurate check on the timing of the programme, and should be capable of letting the director know instantly whether a programme is running to time or not, and the amount by which it is overrunning or underrunning.

She must remind him in advance of any special notes or comments he has made regarding any aspect of the production. And in particular she must continually "feed" the cameramen, sound operators, floor managers, and others with whatever information is vital to them.

In the case of the cameramen, she must call out the number of the next shot, and the camera which will take it. If a cameraman must move his camera to another set as soon as the director has cut away from his shot, the assistant must remind the cameraman of this immediately the cut has been made.

All this information will have previously been supplied as a series of camera cards or "crib cards" to clip alongside the viewfinder. But a television programme is continuous and often fast, and the cameraman must be constantly reminded of coming shots and any important changes of camera position.

In fact, the assistant is one of the busiest people during a television programme, yet she, like everyone else, must not make mistakes. A good assistant is worth her weight in gold to a director, and most directors are honest enough to admit this.

The Vision-Mixer

This is one of the few jobs in television operations that is regularly done both by men and women. In the United States, the job of the vision-mixer or switcher, has been carried out variously by the director, or by the technical director as he coordinates his technical operations crew. In British television, the post has always been a specialist one—formerly an entirely female prerogative. For simplicity let us assume our vision-mixer is of the fair sex.

Although it is the director who decides when a cut from one camera to another will take place—in other words when the picture from one camera will be replaced by the picture from another camera on the viewer's screen—he does not normally perform the actual operation himself, except on outside broadcast units. That is the job of the vision-mixer, and a highly skilled job it is too.

At first sight, the vision-mixing panel may appear formidable. It varies in complexity from small-studio layouts to the ingeniously flexible facilities that the most demanding shows require.

The buttons are normally arranged in horizontal rows, and are connected to the various sources the director might need for his programme. These buttons are numbered to make for easy identification, and numbers one to four would probably be connected to the output from cameras one to four respectively—in a four-camera studio.

If the vision-mixer punches button number one, then Camera One's picture will be transmitted from the studio. In these circumstances we say that the vision-mixer has "cut to Camera One". These cuts from camera to camera are made on the director's instructions, or according to a rehearsed sequence. The vision-mixer can also fade-down one picture as she is fading-up another, so that one "dissolves" into the next. This is also called "cross-fading" or, more usually, just "mixing".

She can fade out the pictures entirely, superimpose one on top of another, and operate a special panel which enables various exciting "wipes" and special transitions to be made.

She can also cut to any film or outside sources that the director might be using, and can often show him, on a special monitor, any unusual superimpositions or contrived shots before he actually needs them on his programme.

Basically, however, her job is to cut or mix to the right source at the right time. And doing just that is an art in itself. The vision-mixer can be regarded as akin to a film editor in the film industry, though she cannot deliberate or have second thoughts.

There is little that the cameraman can do to help her carry out her duties, except to offer his shots in good time. It is very exasperating for a vision-mixer to have to wait for a cameraman to belatedly settle on his shot before she can cut to it.

But the vision-mixer can certainly be of help to the cameraman, if only to minimize the effect of small errors or delays on his part! The good vision-mixer will always look at the next shot on the monitor in front of her before she cuts to it—whatever the director has instructed her to do. If the shot is not quite steady, or if the cameraman is changing lenses, she can delay the cut long enough —a split second perhaps—to enable the cameraman to offer the required shot.

Dramatically speaking, there is a right and wrong moment to cut from one picture to another. Apart from learning this particular art, the vision-mixer must achieve consistency in her work. If a cut from one camera to another has been rehearsed to take place at a certain spot during a programme, it must occur at exactly the same place during transmission.

The cameraman relies on the vision-mixer for this. If she cuts to his camera sooner than he expects, he might well be caught unprepared—he might be preoccupied checking his controls, position, etc.

And cutting to another camera later than rehearsed can be equally disastrous, since this reduces the time available to the cameraman between his shots.

Consistency and alertness—those are the qualities a cameraman likes to see in the vision-mixer. And most vision-mixers possess them. It is a job that makes heavy demands on the nerves, and the position is usually occupied by people with the right qualities—the others fall by the wayside.

There are many other people whose work is so back-room in nature that they are apt to be overlooked when television is being discussed. Most viewers recognize, and to some extent appreciate, the work of the make-up artist (even more important in colour TV) and costume supervisor though they cannot possibly realize the skill and training needed by these specialists to overcome the problems which television presents.

The set designer, who must understand television lenses and angles of view as thoroughly as the cameraman, must be technically as well as artistically minded. In particular he must understand the effect of colour on a black-and-white television tube, and design his sets so that they fall within the acceptable contrast range of the medium. What might be an attractive and colourful set on the studio floor can look disappointingly ineffective on the screen.

But many other specialists never see the limelight. Such people as carpenters, scene-painters, maintenance engineers, graphic artists, film cameramen, film editors and sound "dubbers", telecine operators, recording engineers, researchers, even the office administrative staff—all are essential to the smooth running of a television studio. Without them there would be no worthwhile television programmes.

35

3

STUDIO EQUIPMENT

IT would be impossible to attempt to list the different makes of television camera in use throughout the world. Even if this could be done, the inventory would soon be out of date. New makes and types of camera—and improved versions of existing models— are produced to keep pace with the growth of this increasingly important industry.

Cameras which appeared exciting not so many years ago, now seem to be almost museum pieces—though this is more a reflection on the advances made in recent years than criticism of early equipment.

Studio mountings, too, we find, have improved tremendously of late. Formerly, cameras were mounted on film-industry equipment which had been adapted to television requirements. Gradually, however, equipment became available that had been designed with television in mind, and this helped to raise the standard of television camerawork. The camera became a more versatile instrument than hitherto, and the specialized technique of the television cameraman was born.

For the reasons already outlined, we shall look at cameras and equipment in very general terms only. Nor will there be any attempt to explain in detail the electronic make-up of television cameras, and the technical differences between designs in current use.

That is beyond the scope of this book. We are concerned in the main with the techniques a cameraman needs in order to operate his equipment. And while it is conceded that he must know something of his equipment if he is to operate it to the best advantage, it has never been maintained that the cameraman should possess a detailed knowledge of the electronic side of television before he can become a competent operator.

36

Camera Types

For all its intricate and complicated detail, the television camera is simple enough to understand in principle. It consists basically of two parts: the camera tube and the viewfinder tube; accompanied, of course, by the associated electronic and optical equipment.

The studio scene is focused by the camera lens on to a light-sensitive surface inside the end of the camera tube. The corresponding pattern of electric charges that results from the light and shade of the lens' image is scanned within the camera tube. This scanning process explores the picture charge-pattern in a series of lines, producing the fluctuating electrical voltages we call the video—the television picture.

The second main part of the camera is the viewfinder; a small picture tube showing, in monochrome (even for colour cameras), the picture being generated by the camera. This displays for the cameraman exactly what his lens is seeing—to aid his composition and to enable him to focus sharply upon selected subjects.

The camera lens or lenses may be arranged in several ways. First, the camera could, at its simplest, have just a single fixed lens, like many photographic cameras. For certain purposes this would be quite sufficient. But for most studio and outside broadcast use, it is advantageous to be able to cover narrower or wider angles of view, and so adjust our apparent distance from the scene.

We could screw in each selected lens as we required it, but a better solution is to have them fixed to a large disc attached to the front of the camera. "Swinging" this "turret" rotates it to place any lens required before the camera tube. The lens complement of three or four lenses (occasionally six) usually covers such "standard" lens angles as 9°, 15°, 25°, 35°.

This concept of "standard" lens angles is an arbitrary one, however. Ideally, one would like a single all-purpose lens which could be adjusted to any angle of coverage we sought. Such a design was possible for a limited angular range, but these special lenses were bulky, and of noticeably inferior performance to a series of high-grade fixed lenses. Time brought technological advances, however, and these "zoom lenses" eventually achieved the highest standards of detail and image excellence.

Camera design altered in consequence. So also did camera techniques. Not only could any lens angle required be selected at will, but on changing this angle the picture could "zoom in" or "zoom out" from the subject, as we shall discuss later.

The TV camera tube itself has also changed over the years.

Various tube types have been developed to convert the lens image into a video signal. Each introduces certain improvements, each has its drawbacks. Currently, the vidicon (a cheap, robust, simple type) satisfies cheaper installations: announcers' booths, caption scanners, educational TV, etc. The image orthicon found almost universal application in studios throughout the world for monochrome, and later for colour television. But it has drawbacks, requiring expert attention for best results.

The advent of colour TV in Europe brought the plumbicon to prominence. Its simplicity and excellent picture quality, coupled with new high-grade zoom lens systems, created a new high pictorial standard on the TV screen.

Much of this book refers to the ubiquitous image orthicon tube, and to the turret lens systems. This form of camera design still has wide usage, representing the format from which modern camera techniques developed. Whichever set-up you personally encounter, the studio problems and techniques are here to guide you.

The Camera Tube

Finally, another word about the camera tube. It hates excess light; it is mechanically fragile.

It is common practice for television companies to hire camera tubes, paying a rental for each hour that they are in use in the studio. But if the tubes are ruined by the operators, they must be paid for. And this payment is usually made in addition to the rental charges which have accrued. There are good economic reasons, then, why the cameraman must never be responsible for damaging this item of equipment.

Tubes are normally fitted by experienced video engineers and the cameraman should never be called upon to handle or maintain them in any way. But he can be responsible for damaging them.

Picture Sticking

Early image orthicon camera tubes had two particularly frustrating features. They introduced large black haloes around bright highlights, and they also had a regular habit of "sticking" whenever we held a shot of a bright or high contrast subject for any length of time. Having turned away from such a shot, its image remained "stuck" or imprinted upon our new picture. Although fading away in time, meanwhile it was superimposed, defacing all further shots. In bad cases, the superimposed effect was permanent and the tube ruined.

Subsequent improved camera tube design largely overcame these defects. However, it is safe to say that no camera tube to date, of whatever type, takes kindly to such treatment. "Sticking" is still a danger (particularly as a camera tube ages, or is still warming up to operating temperature after switch-on). Some directors see fit to shoot directly into lamps or reflected highlights, for visual effect, but remember that even the modern plumbicon is not immune to such abuse.

Some versions of image orthicon cameras have a device incorporated into their make-up called image orbit. When switched on, this has the effect of moving the image imperceptibly, and it reduces the risk of the picture "sticking". That is a crude description of its function, and it can be effective in practice. But it is not a foolproof method of guarding against this complaint, and we must look at the cameraman's responsibilities in this direction.

Before doing so, however, it must be pointed out that although the tube can be restored to normal after most "sticks", a severe burn cannot be removed. If this happens the tube will be unsuitable for use, and it must be returned to the manufacturers—and paid for!

Capping-Up

In order to reduce the risk of sticking, the camera is normally provided with a cap that is placed between the tube and the lens. This prevents pictures burning on to the tube when the camera is left unattended. The cap is usually placed in position by activating a knurled wheel or lever at the side of the camera. This operates a disc which is normally mounted within the turret assembly, and which often incorporates a filter wheel.

The disc consists of carefully spaced circular holes which allow uninterrupted passage of light through the lens to the tube. If the "capping-up" device at the side of the camera is then operated, the area between these holes—which is opaque—will prevent any light reaching the tube, and we say that the camera has been "capped-up". Some of these holes are fitted with various filters of graded values, and for this reason the "capping-up" device normally contains some method of telling the cameraman whether he has "capped-up", "uncapped", or brought a filter into play.

The cameraman must never "uncap" a camera without the vision control operator's permission. This operator must adjust certain controls and prepare to expose the pictures before a camera may be "uncapped", and the cameraman can be responsible for damaging the tube if he disregards this instruction.

Whenever the cameraman leaves his camera unattended for any length of time, he must "cap-up" before doing so. The longer a tube is pointed at a subject, the greater the chance of the picture sticking on the tube. This risk is increased if the picture has been focused, but if the subject is very bright—or if it contains some bright highlights—prolonged exposure will cause even a defocused picture to "stick".

Avoiding "Sticks"

Where bright lights appear in shot, reflections from shiny metal, or even strongly-lit white surfaces, the cameraman must take precautions against "sticking".

The cameraman is forced, then, into devising some means of offering his shots during rehearsals and transmissions in such a way that they are *not* continuously sharply focused.

Obviously, he cannot defocus his shots periodically while the picture from his camera is being transmitted. But he can defocus the lens between shots. Provided there is sufficient time between one shot and the next, he should frame his new shot, allow the vision control operator to make his adjustments, and then defocus his picture until just before it is needed.

Some cameramen prefer to keep the shot focused and shake the camera gently to prevent the picture being held static long enough for it to "stick" on the tube. They then steady the camera just before it is needed in the normal way.

This procedure is not necessary between each shot. So much depends on the sticking qualities of the tube, the nature of the subject the camera is shooting, and the length of time between shots. But if there is any danger of the picture sticking on a tube, then the cameraman must adopt one of the methods outlined above.

Burning-Off

If the cameraman must hold a steady shot for so long that the picture "sticks", he must burn this off the tube when he has a minute or so free time during the programme. He should do this by defocusing the lens and pointing the camera at a brightly lit screen. This has the effect of burning off the "stick", although in very bad cases the procedure can take many minutes.

In an emergency, "sticks" are sometimes burnt off by defocusing the lens and pointing the camera at a broad light source. But this can be a dangerous practice, and the cameraman might well make matters worse by burning the light itself on to the tube. That is why he *must* defocus. If in this defocused condition he can still see the outline of the lamp, he must move the camera in a circular motion so that the light never points at one part of the tube for an instant.

If the "stick" must be burnt off in a hurry, it is sometimes a good idea to open the aperture of the lens to its widest point. But the cameraman must remember to restore it to its normal setting before continuing with his shots in the show.

Focusing

The cameraman normally focuses his shots by operating a lever, knurled wheel, capstan, or similar device mounted at the side of the camera, and near the back. On most television cameras this device moves the tube in relation to the lens, though in some systems it is the lens turret that moves.

If someone walks towards the camera, for example, he will become progressively out of focus the nearer he approaches it, unless the cameraman refocuses his picture. In the case quoted, the cameraman would hold sharp focus on the artist during the movement by progressively moving the tube away from the lens.

He would continue to do this until the artist stops moving, or until the tube reaches the end of its travel on the tube carriage. When this point has been reached, the particular lens in use cannot be focused on subjects which are any closer to the camera, and we say that the artist has reached the minimum focusing distance for that lens.

We shall be discussing the technique of focusing later in the book. It is one of the most difficult aspects of camerawork, and the cameraman must acquaint himself as soon as possible with the focusing mechanism installed on his camera, and familiarize himself with the individual mode of operation.

Viewfinders

The picture which the camera is taking is seen by the cameraman in his viewfinder. Most modern viewfinders are electronic, showing only the pictures from the camera in which they are mounted. This is a more satisfactory arrangement than the provision of optical viewfinders, since the cameraman sees not only the areas included in his shots, but also the quality of the picture from a television standpoint.

He sees in his viewfinder roughly the same picture that the viewer receives at home. He does not have to guess how his subjects will appear on the television screen—he can see for himself. Colours, for example, do not always retain the same degree of attraction when converted into monochrome television pictures, and what might appear to be a dominant part of a scene on the studio floor might well fade into insignificance when seen through the camera. Different colours may show as identical grey tones.

Considerations such as these can affect the way in which cameramen frame their shots, and electronic viewfinders must be considered essential for broadcast-standard operation.

The electronic viewfinder presents the cameraman with a small TV picture of his camera's output. He can normally adjust its picture quality to suit himself—though any adjustments he makes will have no effect on the quality of the picture emanating from his camera. This ability to vary the brightness or contrast of the viewfinder picture—apart from being rather convenient to suit individual tastes—is useful in a practical sense. Sometimes the scene that the cameraman is shooting is so dark that he might have difficulty in performing the normal operations of framing and focusing. In these circumstances turning up the brightness of his viewfinder picture will probably show him a little more detail of the scene.

The best type of viewfinder is mounted on top of the camera as a separate item. This can be pivoted up or down to suit the cameraman, enabling him to see the whole of his viewfinder picture wherever he is pointing the camera.

This facility is particularly valuable when the camera is perched high on its dolly, or when it is pointing steeply down or up. Unless the viewfinder is adjustable in this way, the cameraman will have to stand on tip-toe—or kneel on the floor—in order to see into his viewfinder.

The viewfinder picture appears on a small screen. Some viewfinders are provided with a magnifying glass which can be inserted into the viewfinder hood by the cameraman to provide him with a larger picture. The viewfinder hood itself is merely a box-like projection in front of the screen which prevents the studio lights from interfering with the clarity of the viewfinder picture.

Most hoods are padded to enable the cameraman to rest his face against them when looking into the viewfinder, and many cameramen use the pressure of their forehead to help steady the camera when shooting.

When the director has cut to a camera—in other words when the picture from that camera is "on the air"—artists and others in the studio are made aware of this by the fact that a light on the outside of the camera is switched on simultaneously with the cut. Most types of camera are fitted with more than one of these 'tally' lamps, and they are usually red in colour.

The cameraman cannot see these lights, of course, when his head is pressed against the viewfinder hood, and it is important that he is constantly reminded whether or not the director has cut to his camera. Since he will spend much of his time looking at the viewfinder small corresponding indicator lamps are installed beside his viewfinder screen also.

Nearby, within a flick of an eye, will be an indicator too, showing the cameraman the lens or lens angle in use. Where a zoom lens is permanently fitted, this may be a calibrated meter; its needle moving as the lens angle changes.

Where a lens turret is fitted, however, each lens position on the turret is numbered, and as each lens is placed in the taking position in front of the camera tube its turret number lights up inside the cameraman's viewfinder. Provided the cameraman knows which lens corresponds with each turret number, he will know which particular lens is in this taking position.

We shall discuss turret positions and lens mountings in the chapter on television lenses, so we need not consider them further here.

Overscan Control

As we might expect from our previous discussion of "sticking", the light-sensitive face of certain camera tubes gradually deteriorates. Consequently one finds, for example, with image orthicon tubes, that a burnt edge will appear around the sides of the picture when the camera has been in use for some time. To prevent this unsightly highlight being seen by the viewer, these cameras are normally fitted with what is known as an "overscan" control. Once again, it is worth looking at this feature since there are many cameras in use which incorporate this device.

The control is switched to the "on" (overscan) position during rehearsals, and is switched to the "off" or "normal" position for transmissions. Switching to "normal" has the effect of suddenly spreading the picture so that these edges are not included in the frame. After the transmission is over, the switch should be reset to the "overscan" position.

This control, however, presents the cameraman with a problem. When the switch is moved from "overscan" to "normal" the area of the scene visible in the cameraman's shot is reduced—assuming the camera does not move. He must move his camera away from the scene a little, therefore, in order to offer the shot which was agreed during rehearsals.

But during rehearsals he is expected to mark on the floor the position of the camera for each of his shots. These marks will be inaccurate when the control is switched to "normal".

Cameramen devise their own method of marking their camera positions during rehearsals to allow for the difference in their pictures. The adjustment they must make will be a matter of inches only, so most cameramen make their marks during rehearsals a little behind the actual position of the dolly. There can be no hard and fast rule laid down as to the amount by which the rehearsed position will differ from the actual. This is something most cameramen learn to judge very early in their career.

Where the overscan control is not fitted to the camera the cameraman does not need to make these allowances. He must then mark his rehearsed positions accurately since they will be his guides for the positions of his camera during transmission.

Aperture Control

As we shall discuss more fully later (page 61), the amount of light passing through a lens can be adjusted to prevent the camera tube receiving excessive or insufficient light. This can be done in two ways: either by placing a grey-tinted transparent "neutral density filter" over the lens, to reduce image brightness, or by mechanically reducing the effective diameter of the lens-opening.

On some cameras the aperture of the lens can be set manually by the cameraman, and he must always ensure that each lens is correctly set at the required "stop" before each rehearsal and transmission. The "stop" required is determined by the vision control operator, who takes into account such matters as the light level available and the electronic state of the tube.

On other makes of camera, however, the cameraman has no control over the aperture at which the lenses are set. This is governed from the camera control unit. The operator activates a control, and a cogged wheel—set in the centre of the lens turret and in mesh with similar teeth attached to the iris control on each lens—sets the lenses to the "stop" required.

This arrangement is more satisfactory than manually controlled irises. The vision control operator can regulate the quality of his pictures to a finer degree. He does not have to bother the cameraman with requests to open or close the lens iris, nor does he have to accept one position of the iris only for the whole of a programme. This is particularly valuable, of course, in colour TV.

Lining-Up

The 4:3 aspect ratio which is standard in television is achieved by mounting a rectangular mask of the required dimensions in front of the tube—which is round. Before transmissions commence it is common practice to "line-up" each camera, and check that the picture is contained in a 4:3 frame. At the same time, electronic adjustments are made to ensure that the camera is "giving of its best", and that optimum definition is available.

Some cameras have provision for the attachment of a diascope —which is a "line-up" slide with a built-in light source. This slide contains carefully graded lines and tones which enable the VC operator to check the response of the various features of the tube.

Sometimes this "line-up" procedure is carried out against a separate test card, though many studios are content with a quick alignment against known verticals and horizontals, and a focus check on a sharp object.

In colour TV there are additional line-up steps involving colour balance.

Most cameras contain many external and internal adjustable controls, and the best advice that can be given to a cameraman is to leave them severely alone unless requested to do otherwise. If he is not familiar with electronics—or even the basic principles of electricity—he could injure or kill himself through meddling with the camera when it is switched on.

The Panning Head

If the camera is to be a flexible piece of equipment for studio operational work, it cannot be simply clamped to something solid and left there. The cameraman must be free to rotate it vertically and horizontally at will, and we normally call these operations "tilting" and "panning" respectively. We shall discuss these terms in great detail in the chapters on camera movement.

Cameras are normally mounted on panning heads—or pan and tilt heads—which enable the camera to be panned or tilted smoothly, yet remaining horizontally and vertically stable throughout the movement.

The best panning heads are provided with adjustable friction controls, and these enable the cameraman to set the resistance of the panning and tilting motions to suit him personally.

Panning heads are also provided with a means of locking the pan or tilt controls in any desired position, and this facility is extremely useful when the cameraman is called upon to frame such steady subjects as captions and photographs.

Finally, a locking bar or a pair of chains enables the head to be locked rigidly in a horizontal position when the camera must be left unattended for any length of time. This is a sensible safety device, since the camera or tube can be damaged if the camera is accidentally tilted violently.

The cameraman should always lock the head in this way if he must leave his camera for periods longer than about five minutes or so.

The panning head normally contains an angular recess which matches a similarly shaped projection at the base of the camera. The camera is invariably mounted on the panning head by sliding this projection into the slot on the head. Once in place it is secured by pushing a locking bar through the panning head, and this in turn is held firm by a sprung pin.

Cameramen must ensure that the locking bar is rammed home, and the securing pin in place, every time they mount a camera on to a panning head. Failure to do this has resulted in the camera sliding off the head—with embarrassing, costly, or dangerous consequences.

Once mounted, the camera moves in conjunction with the panning head. In order that the head can be panned and tilted, the cameraman is provided with a panning handle. This is usually fitted into a round lug which is attached to the head by a threaded rod. Most of these attachments allow the panning handle to be set at any angle to suit the cameraman.

It is important that the camera is balanced when it is in position on the panning head. A camera that is permanently "front heavy" is a nuisance to the cameraman, since he must fight against the tendency of the camera to dip when he is framing his shots. Ideally, the camera should remain in a horizontal position without the need to lock the pan and tilt controls.

The adjustment is normally contained in the panning head itself. This invariably takes the form of a large, serrated, circular screw-head at the front of the panning head, which is turned to the right to move the camera mounting forward, and to the left to move it back. This enables the cameraman to balance the camera to a very fine degree, and the cameraman must never neglect this aspect of his work particularly when camera attachments are fitted (e.g. prompters, image inverters etc.).

The panning head must always be kept in a good state of maintenance, since no cameraman can be responsible for good camerawork if the head is badly adjusted or worn. But it is his responsibility to report faults, since in a large television organization it is impossible for maintenance staff to test all equipment every day. They rely on information from the operators.

Studio Mountings

The studio camera must be mobile. Fixed camera positions place crippling restrictions on the director, and these are adopted only in very small studios which confine themselves to such programmes as news items and station announcements.

For all general studio work, therefore, cameras are mounted on "dollies" which can be moved about the studio. These vary in design from simple pedestals that are pushed by the cameraman, to electrically-driven, highly versatile dollies which need the services of one or more trackers.

The variety of dollies in current use throughout the world makes a detailed description of each type impossible. In fact, it is not really necessary for the cameraman to have at his fingertips an intimate knowledge of every piece of camera equipment. Studio mountings can be classified into a number of broad groups, and the individual peculiarities of the dollies within these groups will easily be mastered by any intelligent cameraman in a short space of time.

Pedestal Dollies

The simplest form of studio mounting is the pedestal dolly. This consists of a three-wheeled base supporting a central column, which can be raised or lowered by the cameraman. The cameraman must have freedom to move this column smoothly and unobtrusively, and it is rather important that the camera can be set at any height without the need for a separate locking device. There are many methods of providing this facility of varying camera height, since manufacturers have developed their individual solutions to the technical problems involved.

Earlier pedestals were wound up and down by means of a handle, which meant that these moves could not be attempted by the cameraman while his camera was "on the air". Further, many types had to be locked when the required height had been reached.

But the modern pedestal has been designed to meet the cameraman's requirements. The column is so finely counterbalanced that it can be moved with fingertip pressure from the cameraman, yet will remain at any height without the need for a separate locking device. Some models enable the cameraman to adjust the height of the column while moving his camera by merely exerting a slight pressure in the required direction.

We can look at some examples of the methods used by the makers of these dollies to provide an extendable column.

Pressurized gas is used in a popular type of pedestal dolly, and the cameraman controls the height of this column by pressing a pedal with his foot and then raising or lowering the camera to the desired height. When needed, this pedal can be locked in the "open" position to enable the cameraman to adjust the height while moving the dolly. The weight of the camera and any accessories is counterbalanced against the pressure of the gas by removing or adding lead weights, which are located in a special holder near the top of the column. When heavy accessories are added (e.g. prompters), it may be necessary to release some of the gas (de-gassing) to provide correct column pressure.

Another form of pedestal dolly incorporates a spring-loaded column. The tension on this spring can be varied quite easily by simply operating the special handle provided. Once the tension has been correctly adjusted, the column can be raised and lowered with little effort. But if the camera must be removed from the dolly it is essential that it is firmly locked according to the maker's instructions. Without the weight of the camera to resist the pressure of the spring, the column will fly to the top of its travel with potentially dangerous consequences. In fact, if the dolly is to be left without a camera for any length of time the tension should be completely removed from the spring.

Another popular make of dolly relies on a system of counterbalancing weights suspended within the framework of the column. This type is particularly smooth in operation, and it is simple to maintain since there are few parts which can give trouble.

Dollies on which the height of the column is controlled by an electric motor are seen in some studios. These are only reasonably successful—from the operational point of view—if the speed of the column movement can be varied by the cameraman. Provided the motor is regularly maintained, the operation can be quite smooth. But if this is neglected the noise of the motor can be disturbing, and the beginning and end of each movement can be accompanied by a jerk—which is rather disturbing to the cameraman.

These are typical examples of the more popular pedestals in modern use, though there are others giving reliable service in studios throughout the world. The cameraman will soon become accustomed to the characteristics of the type of dolly installed at his studio.

He must pay particular attention to the safety precautions that must be taken when the dolly is relieved of the weight of the camera. These vary from model to model, and must always be obeyed under these circumstances.

The panning head is normally attached to the top of the column by a series of bolts, though some types of column provide for a clamping ring or similar device.

Steering the Pedestal Dolly

The wheels of the dolly can usually be set to two conditions—known as "crab" and "dolly". In the "crab" position—the normal working state—all three wheels are driven in the same direction by the steering device. The dolly can then be moved forwards, sideways, or diagonally with equal ease and smoothness. In the "dolly" position one wheel only is steered, and this is mainly used to rotate the pedestal into a more advantageous position for the cameraman.

The steering device might be a handle at the side of the dolly, or a large, horizontal ring mounted just below the camera. Ring-steering is the more convenient method, since the cameraman can control the direction of his pedestal from wherever he stands in relation to it. If the dolly is provided with a steering handle, however, the cameraman must always endeavour to keep this near his free hand, and he can waste much time changing the condition of his dolly from "crab" to "dolly" and back again to achieve this.

Each type of dolly has its advantages and disadvantages, and each is ideally suitable for a given set of working conditions. So much depends on the kind of programmes the studio normally presents, the amount of work expected from the dollies, whether or not they will be used in conjunction with other, more elaborate mountings, and so on. Points such as these should be given care-full consideration before deciding on the model to be used in a studio.

The maximum and minimum heights at which the camera can be placed differ greatly from one type of pedestal to the next, and this is another matter which must be taken into account when deciding on the merits or otherwise of a particular dolly.

Small Camera Crane

When the pedestal is much higher or lower than the cameraman's own head height, his problems of smooth camera operation increase enormously. To track the pedestal precisely at such extremes, while focusing and adjusting composition is just not practicable.

To permit height adjustments on a moving camera, the small camera crane was designed. Again, it was originally devised for the film studio, and has become adapted and elaborated for television.

This is—to put it simply—a four-wheeled truck, with provision for the cameraman to sit behind the camera which is placed at the front. The camera and cameraman are invariably mounted on a pivoted arm which can be raised or lowered by various means. The dolly itself is driven or pushed by one or more trackers, who are sometimes responsible for controlling the height of the pivoted arm.

The simplest type is the manually-tracked dolly which is pushed and steered by one tracker. He also raises and lowers the arm by means of a wheel, and can sometimes cause the arm to rotate about its base providing a "gibbing" or "tonguing" action, slewing the camera head from side to side—which is dealt with in later chapters.

Movement with this type of dolly is relatively slow—so much depends on the strength of the tracker and the weight of the cameraman!—but very smooth movements are possible nonetheless. The manually-tracked dolly is ideal for providing a suitable progression in the cameraman's career from pedestal to the more elaborate forms of trackable dollies.

The steering wheel—mounted in front of the tracker who stands at the back of the dolly—normally acts on the rear wheels only. Varying the height during a shot is not always a practical proposition with this type of dolly, unless the movement is performed slowly. The mechanical nature of the controls tends to cause the camera to rise and fall in a series of disturbing shakes.

The motorized dolly is a four-wheeled dolly, driven—as its name suggests—by an electric motor. The operating problems and techniques connected with this apparatus are discussed in detail in the chapter on Later Techniques.

It is a vast improvement over the manually-tracked dolly so far as the tracker is concerned. He merely stands on a special

50

platform at the rear of the dolly, steers with a large wheel, and lets the motor do the work. On some early models he was also responsible for operating a separate motor which controlled the height of the pivoted arm.

Later designs give the cameraman the height control instead. This increases his movement coordination, but now he must take particular care to avoid crushing nearby obstacles when preoccupied with his viewfinder picture.

In the hands of experienced trackers and cameramen these dollies are extremely versatile. The speed at which they can be driven around the studio is rather startling when first seen, but this increases the number of shots a camera can be expected to take during a show. The director can use his cameras to provide the coverage he wants on all his sets, with a minimum of time delay.

Although the beginning of each movement is invariably accompanied by a slight jerk as the motor is brought into play, this can be nullified by an experienced crew, and smooth movements are possible at all speeds.

The Mole Crane

Without doubt, however, the most exciting studio dolly is the crane. This piece of equipment has been used by the film world for many years, and it soon found its way into television studios as this industry matured. The most common model to be seen in British television was the Mole Richardson type, and it is often referred to as the Mole Crane, or simply the "Mole".

It consists of a four-wheeled dolly having a central, vertical column. Resting on this column—and pivoting freely about the mounting—is a heavy metal arm which extends beyond the front of the dolly by three feet or so. A platform is attached to the front end of the arm, on which rests the mounting for the camera. A seat is provided for the cameraman.

The rear end of this pivoted arm comprises a bucket into which lead weights can be slotted to counterbalance the combined weight of the camera and cameraman. This bucket is provided with grips to enable a tracker to swing the arm through 360 degrees of horizontal movement. The crane is driven by an electric motor, and is steered by a wheel or T-shaped handle acting on the rear wheels.

Early models required the services of three trackers: a driver, a "swinger", and a steerer. But later developments of the crane provide a steering and driving device at the rear of the dolly—operated by one tracker—and this has reduced the number of trackers to two.

Although a crane may have a small guide monitor attached, to aid the tracker and "swinger", most cameramen control their crew's actions by precise hand signals. Operating the crane—either as a cameraman or as a tracker—calls for a special skill and technique. This is discussed more fully later in the book, so we need consider this dolly only briefly here.

The central column can normally be raised by pumping a special handle located near its base. This enables the camera to be elevated to a height of about nine feet, which is superior to any other dolly we have discussed here.

Crane Safety Precautions

The crane weighs a couple of tons and is capable of over 5 mph. In inexperienced hands it can be a dangerous weapon, and it should always be manned by experienced or carefully supervised trackers.

Since the arm is counterbalanced to a fine degree, it will be obvious that the cameraman must never vacate his position at the front of the arm without warning; this sudden reduction of weight at the front will cause the bucket end of the arm to crash on to the "swinger's" platform. In order to avoid this eventuality, a solenoid locking device is incorporated in the dolly which is activated by a switch under the cameraman's seat. This has the effect of locking the arm firmly as soon as the cameraman rises from his seat.

A mechanical lock is also provided, and this should always be operated before the cameraman leaves the dolly. No cameraman should ever step off the crane without permission from his trackers, and they must always ensure that the arm is safely locked before giving this permission.

Some cameramen disconnect the solenoid control—especially during transmissions—since this allows them to stand on their foot platforms for steeply down-angled shots. This is a dangerous practice, and it is not to be recommended.

Because it is relatively easy for the locking device to be accidentally unlocked—with consequences that can be imagined—many trackers hold the arm in place with chains or cables whenever the dolly is left unattended. These precautions may seem a little elaborate, but there have been cases of serious injury caused by carelessness. The crane is not an inherently dangerous piece of equipment, however. Operated by intelligent, experienced trackers it provides opportunities for uninhibited, exciting camerawork.

We have looked at the four broad groups of studio mountings—pedestals, manually-tracked, motorized, and crane dollies—and have singled out some points of interest. There are many types within these groups, and there are models that fall between them.

An example of the latter is the "Heron" which has recently made its mark in British television. This is a compact combination of a motorized dolly and a crane. Hydraulic power is used to raise and lower the camera, and the dolly can be put into a condition of "crab"—which compensates for the fact that the camera cannot be "gibbed" to right or left.

Many forms of dolly have not been mentioned, quite deliberately. Any attempt at a complete list would be impossible. Cameramen soon familiarize themselves with their dollies, and form their individual opinions of the merits and demerits of the types they handle. To a large extent, of course, the type of dollies he encounters will depend on their availability, the type of production, and the techniques the director uses.

Revolutionary and exciting dollies are already in the prototype stage. An example is the Peregrine. Here the cameraman sits alongside his tracker and operates, by remote control, a camera mounted at the end of a pivoted arm. The cameraman's "viewfinder" is in the form of a monitor mounted in front of him and he is not forced, therefore, into physical contortions in order to cope with difficult and unusual camera movements. This type of dolly gives rise to the need for new techniques to be devised by television cameramen, and the exciting possibilities of the future can only be imagined at this stage.

The cameraman is advised never to miss the opportunity of operating new or strange pieces of equipment. Anything he can add to his store of knowledge and experience will help broaden the limits of his technique and skill.

4

BASIC OPTICS

THIS chapter is the only part of the book that deals entirely with preparatory theory. But this should not discourage anyone from reading it. Although the would-be cameraman does not need to study the subject of optics in detail, there is no doubt that an understanding of the basic principles should be part of every cameraman's make-up.

Optical terms are used daily in television operations. There are optical laws which help the cameraman solve many of the problems connected with his work. He should understand what happens to light waves when they pass through a lens: why depths of field are limited: what is meant by focal lengths and f numbers.

Some of these terms will be familiar to many readers. But for the benefit of the newcomer, the subject of optics has been treated from basic principles to the behaviour of light passing through lenses—and no further. Every attempt has been made to explain the principles simply and clearly.

The more ambitious student is advised to study some of the many books on the market which deal with optics in a more informed and comprehensive manner. Here we shall deal briefly with only those aspects of the subject which concern the television cameraman.

When light waves, travelling through air, come into contact with another medium—e.g. glass, water, silver, another gas— there are three ways in which they can behave. They can be reflected, refracted, or absorbed.

Reflection

A line drawn at right-angles to a mirror is called the "normal". A ray of light travelling towards the mirror is called the "incident ray", and when it has been reflected it is called the "reflected ray". If the incident ray travels along the normal, the reflected ray will travel back along the normal. If the incident ray strikes the mirror at an angle of 20 degrees to the normal, the reflected ray will leave at the same angle of 20 degrees, but on the other side of the normal.

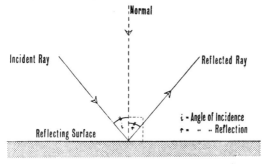

Fig. I. Behaviour of light wave striking a reflecting surface—such as a mirror. *Note:* Angle *i* = angle *r*.

From this we have the two basic laws of reflection.
1. The angle of incidence = the angle of reflection ($i = r$).
2. The incident ray, the reflected ray, and the normal all lie on the same plane.

Let us imagine that an object is placed in front of a mirror, and at an angle to the normal. The incident ray will meet the mirror at an angle i to the normal, and the reflected ray will leave at an angle r to the normal. If the eye is placed in the line of the reflected ray, it will see an image of the object in the mirror. This image will appear to lie behind the mirror, and it will have certain important characteristics.

In the first place, it will lie as far behind the reflecting surface as the object does in front.

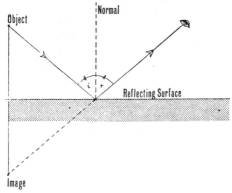

Fig. 2. The virtual image lies as far behind the mirror as the object does in front.

Secondly, because it is an image that cannot be picked up on a screen placed in front of the mirror, it is called a "virtual image". If it could be seen on a screen, it would be called a "real image".

Thirdly, the image is not vertically inverted. It is referred to as being "erect".

Fourthly, it is not magnified or diminished in size, compared to the object. We say that it has "unity magnification".

Lastly, the image is laterally inverted; that is, the right-hand side of the object is the left-hand side of the image.

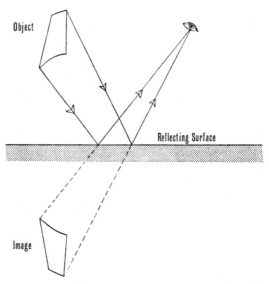

Fig. 3. If the image is studied from the position of the eye in the diagram, it will be seen that this image is vertically erect, laterally inverted and of unity magnification.

So we refer to the image formed by placing an object in front of a mirror as being virtual, erect, of unity magnification, and laterally inverted. And it lies as far behind the mirror as the object does in front.

Refraction

When a ray of light, travelling through air, enters a denser medium—glass, water, etc.—its velocity is retarded. This has the effect of bending the ray of light towards the normal. If the ray passes completely through the denser medium and re-enters the air it is bent away from the normal as it emerges. This emergent ray, as it is called, is parallel to the incident ray.

56

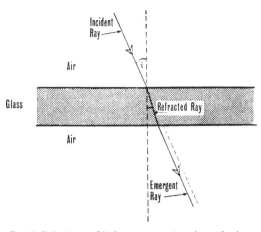

Fig. 4. Behaviour of light wave passing through glass.
Note that the refracted ray is bent towards the normal
and the emergent ray is parallel to the incident ray.

Each transparent medium has what is known as a "refractive index". This is given the symbol μ, and is the result of dividing $\sin i$ by $\sin r$; where i = angle of incidence, and r = angle of refraction. If we regard the refractive index for air as 1, the refractive index for water is 1·3, and for glass, between 1·5 and 1·7.

The amount of displacement of a ray passing through glass depends on the refractive index of the glass, the thickness of the glass and the angle of incidence.

If the incident ray enters the refracting medium along the line of the normal, it is not refracted.

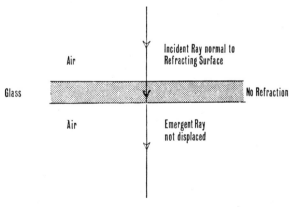

Fig. 5. A ray of light entering glass along the normal is not refracted.

But it should be noted that when the ray is refracted, the incident ray, the refracted ray, and the normal all lie on the same plane.

Critical Angle

If a refracted ray passes through glass at an angle of approximately 41 degrees to the normal, it runs along the surface of the glass when it emerges. This condition is known as "grazing emergence", and the angle of approximately 41 degrees is known as the "critical angle".

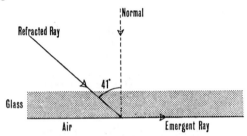

Fig. 6. When the refracted ray makes the "critical angle" with the normal, the emergent ray travels along the surface of the glass.

If, however, the refracted ray makes an angle with the normal which is greater than the critical angle, the ray does not emerge. It is "internally reflected".

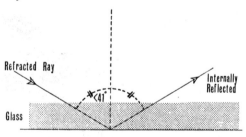

Fig. 7. When angle between refracted ray and the normal is greater than the "critical angle", there is no emergent ray.

Absorption

Where a ray of light meets a medium which is so dense that it will not allow the light to pass through, or which has virtually no reflective properties, the amount of light not reflected is absorbed. This need not concern us any further, since we are more interested in the behaviour of light in relation to glass.

Convex Lenses

Rays of light parallel to the principal axis converge at a point on the principal axis. This point is the principal focus (P) and its distance from the centre of the lens represents the focal length of the lens. For all practical purposes, rays of light from an object at infinity converge on the principal focus, which lies each side of the lens, along the principal axis.

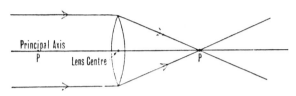

Fig. 8. With the convex lens, rays of light converge at the principal focus (P).

The image is real and inverted, and whether it is diminished or magnified is determined by the object distance. As the object is moved nearer the lens, the image size increases.

If the object is placed between the lens and the principal focus, however, no real image is produced. In this case the image is virtual, erect, and magnified.

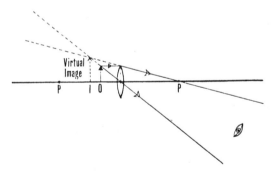

Fig. 9. When the object is between the principal focus and the lens, the image is erect, magnified and virtual.

We shall be coming back to convex and multiple lenses later, but we must first examine the effect of concave lenses.

Concave Lenses

These lenses cause rays of light falling on them to diverge, and produce images which are virtual, erect, and diminished. The

59

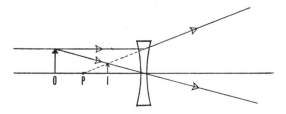

Fig. 10. With the concave lens, rays of light diverge and form an image that is erect, diminished and virtual. *Note:* The image always lies between (P) and the lens.

image always lies between the principal focus and the centre of the lens, whatever the object distance.

Telephoto Lenses

A telephoto lens is a lens having multiple elements. These are so arranged that they provide an effective focal length which is longer than the physical length of the lens.

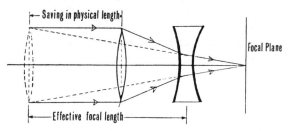

Fig. 11. The telephoto lens gives a long effective focal length with saving in physical length.

These lenses make it possible to equip cameras with long focal lenses without the inconvenient physical lengths which would otherwise be necessary.

Zoom Lenses

These are lenses with multiple, movable elements, so constructed that they provide a continuously variable focal length over a certain range (e.g. 4 to 20 in.). In other words, moving the control mechanism sets the lens to any focal length within the range of the instrument. When the lens has been focused on an object at a considerable distance, the image remains in sharp focus throughout the full range of the lens. No focus correction is necessary as the lens is zoomed in or out, but, as we shall see in a later chapter, this is not the same as moving a lens towards or away from a subject.

Some zoom lenses are provided with two ranges. By moving a lever the lens can provide a variable focal length range of either 4 to 20 in. or 8 to 40 in., for example.

Transmission Factor

When light passes through a lens, a certain amount is absorbed and internally reflected, so that a smaller amount of light emerges than originally entered, The ratio of the light emerging to the incident light is called the transmission factor. Taking the value of the incident light as 1, the transmission factor will always be less than 1, and is usually given as 0·9 (90 per cent) or 0·75 (75 per cent), for example, according to the light loss.

In the case of lenses having multiple elements (such as telephoto and zoom lenses) the transmission factor can be as low as 0·6. In order to keep the transmission factor as high as possible, lenses are coated with a transparent medium (such as magnesium fluoride). This is known as blooming or coating the lens.

Through reducing internal light-scatter, this markedly improves the overall transmission factor, and the contrast of the image.

f-Numbers

Incorporated in each lens is the diaphragm, or iris. This is a metallic device consisting of overlapping leaves. These are so arranged that they can be spread or closed in such a way that they always provide a circular opening through which the incident light can pass. If the iris is opened up, more light passes through the lens.

In order that the amount of light passing through the lens can be controlled, there has to be some form of measurement on the iris control. The most common method is the use of f numbers.

The f number for any given opening of the iris is found by dividing the focal length of the lens by the diameter of the iris.

If a lens having a focal length of 8 in. has its iris at a diameter of 1 in., the f number is 8. We say, in this case, that the lens has been set at f 8. If a 12 in. lens has an iris diameter of 1½ in., it too is set at f 8, and allows the same amount of light to pass through it as the 8 in. lens which is set at f 8.

These f numbers, therefore, provide a convenient method of setting the irises of different lenses so that, theoretically, at least, they will all admit an equal amount of light.

In the case of the 8 in. lens, if the iris diameter is reduced from

1 to $\frac{3}{4}$ in., a simple calculation gives us an f number of 11 (more or less). It will be found that the amount of light entering the lens at this iris setting is reduced to about half its former value (because the lens area is reduced by that amount).

If the iris is set to admit double the amount of light entering the lens at f 8 the lens diameter becomes about $1\frac{1}{2}$ in. (to give double the area). The f number then works out at $5 \cdot 6$.

It can be seen that a set of numbers can be provided on the iris control to enable us to increase or decrease, by set amounts, the quantity of light passing through the lens.

It can also be seen that if we open the iris to admit more light, the f number becomes smaller. (A lens set at f 8 admits less light than a lens set at f 5·6.)

It will be convenient, therefore, if we can mark on the iris control a set of numbers which will tell us when we are progressively doubling the amount of light entering the lens. The most common range of f numbers marked on iris controls is as follows: 2; 2·8; 4; 5·6; 8; 11; 16; 22. If we open the iris from f 4 to f 2·8 we double the amount of light entering the lens. We usually refer to this as "opening up the lens one stop". If we move the iris control from f 5·6 to f 8, we say that we are "stopping down one stop". Some lenses are calibrated in half stops, and this makes for very accurate settings of the iris control. Setting the lens at f 6·3, for example, allows 50 per cent more light to pass through the lens than at f 8.

Circle of Confusion and Depth of Field

If a lens is correctly focused on a pin-point object, it throws a sharp image of that object on to the focal plane. (In television, this is the face of the camera tube.) If the object is moved closer to or farther away from the lens the image, instead of being a sharp point, becomes a circular blob. The diameter of this circle increases as the object is brought nearer the lens. Provided the diameter of this circle of confusion, as it is called, is kept within certain limits, however, the image can be said to be in acceptable focus.

This means that the object must be placed within the limits of the nearest and farthest distances from the lens at which the circle of confusion remains at acceptable size. The distance between these two limits is called the depth of field. By this we mean that although an object should be at a definite position to be sharply focused in the picture, it will remain in acceptable focus if placed anywhere between these limits.

62

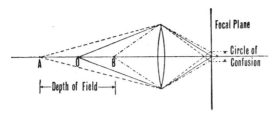

Fig. 12. Where the diameter of the circle of confusion does not exceed acceptable limits, distance A — B = depth of field. O = object.

In practice, the object can always be moved farther away from the lens than towards it. In other words, there is always a greater depth of field behind an object in sharp focus than there is in front of it.

Hyperfocal Distance

If an object at infinity is in sharp focus on the focal plane, then the distance from the lens to the nearest point in *acceptable* focus is called the hyperfocal distance.

If the lens is focused on an object placed at the hyperfocal distance, then everything from infinity to half the hyperfocal distance is in acceptable focus. Obviously, if we can reduce the hyperfocal distance we shall increase the depth of field of the lens.

The hyperfocal distance is the focal length of the lens multiplied by the diameter of the iris, divided by the diameter of the circle of confusion. If we wish to make the hyperfocal distance smaller—in other words, increase the depth of field—we must either use a lens of shorter focal length, or reduce the diameter of the iris, i.e. "stop down".

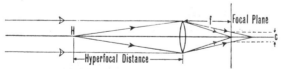

Fig. 13. When the object is at infinity, (H) is the nearest point at which an acceptably sharp image will be produced. The distance from the lens to (H) is the hyperfocal distance.

From this we have the following facts: a short focal length lens has a greater depth of field than a long focal length lens, for a given distance from lens to subject; when we "stop down" a lens we increase the depth of field; and when we "open up" a lens we reduce the depth of field.

63

It is also a fact that the farther an object is placed from a lens, the greater will be the depth of field both in front of and behind the object. We shall be discussing the application of these optical facts throughout the rest of the book. But the cameraman will have a better understanding of these principles if he experiments with lenses and object distances himself.

The subject of optics has been dealt with very simply in this chapter. Every effort has been made to confine the information to those aspects of the subject which the cameraman should learn. As mentioned earlier, there are many books which deal with the subject more comprehensively than we have attempted to do here. But an understanding of the subject matter of this chapter should help the cameraman over most of the optical obstacles he might encounter early in his career.

5

LENSES

WHY do we need choices of lens angles? Why are multi-lens turrets or zoom lenses fitted to television cameras? The answer lies in increased productional flexibility.

Since three or more cameras are used simultaneously on the majority of television programmes, it is not always possible to move a camera close to an artist in order to obtain a close-up. The camera might enter a wide shot being taken by another camera, for example. In this case, the camera taking the close-up will need a lens with a narrow angle of view (i.e. a long focal length).

Similarly, due to restricted studio space, a camera should have a lens giving a wide angle of view (i.e. short focal length) if a wide shot of a set is required, despite restricted camera distance.

A camera with a rapidly selectable choice of lens angles offers the director increased shot opportunities. The cameraman can change his shot from a close-up to a wide shot, within seconds, without moving his camera. By using the range of lenses on his camera intelligently, and with very small changes of camera position, the cameraman can provide a very wide variety of shots on any scene.

Further, as we shall see later, the characteristics of wide-angle lenses differ from those of narrow-angle lenses, and there is always a right lens for a particular shot. If the camera were equipped with one lens only, too many shots would be a matter of compromise.

Angle of View and Focal Length

When we talk of the angle of view of a lens we usually mean the horizontal angle of view. But the lens has a vertical angle of view too and this figure can be very important to set designers in particular. They must design their sets so that they are high enough, as well as wide enough to prevent cameras from seeing past the confines of the sets.

Since the aspect ratio in television is four horizontal to three

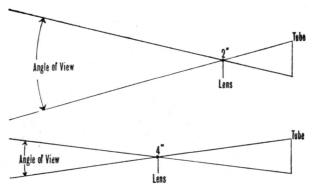

Fig. 14. A simple method of remembering the relationship between focal length and angle of view of a lens. Short focal length
= wide angle of view. Long focal length = narrow angle of view.

vertical, it follows that the ratio between the horizontal and
vertical angles of view will be 4:3. A lens with a horizontal angle
of view of 24 degrees will have a vertical angle of view of 18
degrees, and so on. The lens itself, of course, has an equal angle of
view in all directions. The restriction lies in the picture as finally
presented, i.e. the shape of the masking of the camera tube and the
TV scanning pattern.

Whenever the term "angle of view" is mentioned in this book,
it must be taken to refer to the horizontal angle of view, unless
otherwise stated.

A lens can be identified by referring either to its focal length
or to its angle of view. For purposes of comparison, it would be
convenient if a focal length of X inches always meant an angle of
view of Y degrees. But this is not so in practice.

The size of the photocathode and mask of the camera tube
varies between one type of camera and another. A 3 in. lens on
one camera might have an effective angle of view of 25 degrees;
on another camera the angle of view, with the same focal length
lens, might well be 33 degrees.

Where one type of camera only is used in a television studio, it
does not matter, of course, which method is used to describe a lens.
But when we are considering the television industry in general, as
we are doing here, we can avoid ambiguity only if we refer to
lenses by their angle of view. An angle of view of 25 degrees means
what it says, whatever the focal length of the lens. Whenever
necessary, however, an indication of typical focal lengths will be
included along with angles of view.

But to confuse the issue a little, some lenses are always identified by the focal length. The long focal length lenses, normally used on outside broadcasts, are invariably referred to as 17 in. or 40 in. lenses, and not by their angles of view.

The actual lens angles we shall require will depend, as we shall see, upon the studio mechanics, the scenic illusion we are seeking, and so on. Modern zoom lenses may offer a wide choice—a continuous range from 5 to 50 degrees. The four most common lenses on a four-lens turret are those with focal lengths of 2 in., 3 in., 5 in., and 8 in., giving approximate angles of view of 35 degrees, 25 degrees, 15 degrees, and 9 degrees.

There are advantages and disadvantages attached to the use of each angle, and the cameraman must understand these if he is to use his equipment to the best advantage. There might well be times when he will be forced to use the wrong angle for a shot; this might be due to constricted studio space, or the nearness of other cameras and studio equipment. But whenever possible he must always try to use the right angle for the shot in hand.

The Wide-Angle Lens

With an angle of view of around 30 degrees or over, this is the lens to use where a vast area has to be included in a shot. It can impart a feeling of breadth and depth which does not exist on the actual set. Since all wide-angle lenses exaggerate perspective, near objects appear very large and distant objects very small. This gives the impression that things are nearer or farther away from the camera than they really are. Distances are exaggerated, and a false sense of spaciousness imparted.

Movement towards or away from the camera can appear quite startling. Artists appear to grow rapidly as they approach the camera, and this creates the feeling that they are moving faster than they really are. The effect of camera movement, too, is amplified. Fast moves, when using this lens, can be exciting.

Another feature of the wide-angle lens is that it "irons out" any small irregularities in camera movement. If the floor is not absolutely smooth, or if the camera dolly is a little worn and there is likely to be some camera shake, the wide-angle lens is the best lens to use.

But this lens should not be used merely to cover up bad camerawork. In the hands of an experienced operator, with first-class equipment, smooth, exciting, and sometimes beautiful movement is possible. But a bad cameraman can do bad work just as easily with this lens as with any other. Small irregularities will be minimized—but not ineptitude.

For a given distance from camera to subject, wide-angle lenses provide a greater depth of field than lenses with narrower angles of view. Camera or artist movement can be covered with little need to correct focus. This leads many cameramen to use wide-angle lenses as often as they possibly can but the practice is to be deplored. The use of a wide-angle lens for many shots is contrary to the principles of competent, artistic camerawork. And it is an admission of his own lack of skill if a cameraman attempts to take as many shots as possible with this lens.

Although this might appear to be the ideal lens to use for all camera movement, this is not so. As we know, it has the effect of exaggerating perspective, and this leads to unflattering distortion of facial features if the lens is moved close to an artist. The nose, which is nearest the lens, looms larger than life in the foreground. And if the artist is shot from a low angle, he presents a very heavy-jowled appearance. This is discussed in greater detail later in the book, but it is as well to mention it here.

If the cameraman must track the camera from a wide shot of an artist to a close-up, the "normal" lens, of 20 to 26 degrees, should be used. Smooth camera movement will still be possible, but there will be no appreciable distortion when the close-up has been framed.

In very small studios wide-angle lenses have to be used where narrower angle lenses would give more accurate scale, if there is insufficient room to enable the camera to be moved back from the set, and for the correct lens to be used. In these circumstances the cameraman must pay careful attention to the position and height of his camera for every shot. He must avoid unreal perspective and facial distortion. He must resist any temptation to track his camera close to an artist—it is far better to settle for a safe mid-shot than to attempt a more ambitious, ugly close-up.

The Normal Lens

This lens, with an angle of view of between 20 and 26 degrees, is probably used more than any other in television. It is the maid of all work. It has no real vices, such as perspective distortion, and it does not call for an exceptionally large area in which to provide effective wide shots.

The extent of a scene included in its angle of view would be what the lay-man would expect to see. It does not provide unexpectedly close detail, nor does it give an exaggerated wide shot. In fact it has no surprises, and it is the lens which would probably be fitted to a camera if there were provision for one lens only. In fact, a lens of approximately 24 degrees is invariably found on film cameras, whenever one lens only is fitted—hence the term "normal lens" used here.

As mentioned earlier, the cameraman should use this lens if he is asked to track his camera close to an artist's features. The amount of focus correction needed with this type of lens will not be excessive, and all in all it is very pleasant and effective to use. Little else need be said about it: it can be used as often as circumstances allow. However, due to the multi-camera set-up in most television shows, tight shots of artists and detail will have to be taken with intermediate and narrow-angle lenses.

The Intermediate Lens

This is used to provide a shot which is wider than a close-up and tighter than a medium long shot, from a given camera position. It has an angle of view of between 14 and 17 degrees, which is also extremely useful for shooting captions. It provides a camera to caption-board distance sufficiently small that people will not inadvertently walk in front of the camera, but not so small that there is danger of the camera casting a shadow over the caption.

There is smaller depth of field available with this lens than with a normal or wide-angle lens, and the cameraman must take care when he is asked to perform any movement with it. It is not a suitable lens to use when camera movement is needed, for a number of reasons.

The problem of holding focus is increased: flaws in camera movement will be noticeable, indeed exaggerated; and there will be little increase in the size of an artist as the camera moves towards him. This has the effect of minimizing the feeling of movement. Since this will be inevitably accompanied by distracting camera shake, together with an increased focusing problem for the cameraman, these lenses should be avoided when camera movement is contemplated.

But the intermediate lens has a definite place in the range of camera lenses, and is rather like a little finger—you would miss it if it were taken away.

The Narrow-Angle Lens

The angle of view of this lens is only 8 to 10 degrees and it is almost invariably used to provide apparent close-ups, while still keeping the camera some distance away from a subject. But this lens has certain limitations, and requires some care when it is used.

In the first place, it has a restricted depth of field. The cameraman's focusing problems are greater, then, and the slightest movement of an artist towards or away from the camera requires some focus correction on the majority of shots taken with this lens.

Camera movement with a narrow-angle lens must be regarded as being out of the question. Apart from the fact that there is little impression of movement towards the camera, even for long tracks of the camera, it is impossible to keep the shot steady. Flaws in camera movement are greatly exaggerated.

This lens generally has a minimum focusing distance of about three feet. This means that it is impossible to focus on any subject which is less than this distance from the lens. In theory, a lens can focus right down to a distance equal to its focal length, but to do so it has to be moved well forward from the focal plane (the camera tube). Few cameras permit such a long extension of the lens, so the minimum focusing distance is usually much greater in practice than in theory. The difference is less, however, in the wider angle lenses. The minimum focusing distance of a 24-degree lens is, in practice about 7 in., a vast improvement over the narrow-angle lens.

But, despite these limitations, narrow-angle lenses are an essential part of the cameraman's equipment. Without them many close shots of artists and other details would be impossible.

When used at great distances from subjects they present an unnatural lack of perspective. There is little difference in size between near and distant objects, and this is interpreted by the human eye and brain to mean that these objects are very close together. In other words, narrow-angle lenses tend to close up these planes in any shot, and they give no feeling of depth and perspective.

There is, however, one exception to the rule that narrow-angle lenses can give no feeling of perspective to a shot. This utilizes the fact that the depth of field is limited. If a close-up of an artist, who is standing about twelve feet in front of a set, is taken with a narrow-angle lens, the background will be outside the depth of field. It will be diffused in the picture. This helps to direct the viewer's attention to the close-up of the artist, since there is no distracting background detail. The artist will stand out sharply against this out-of-focus background, and this adds an attractive sense of depth to the shot. This technique is known as differential focusing, and is the only occasion when a narrow-angle lens can be used to give a feeling of perspective depth to a shot.

Additional Lenses

Where standard turret lenses do not cover sufficiently wide or narrow angles, either clip-on supplementaries, or replacement lenses may be substituted. Obviously, these additional lenses have either very wide or very narrow angles of view.

The Very Wide-Angle Lens (Angle of view over 45 degrees.)

This lens enables us to encompass a wide field of view, enhancing breadth and depth where there is, in fact, very little available. All the advantages and disadvantages of wide-angle lenses are amplified. Camera movement can be ultra-smooth; little focus correction is needed; the impression of movement is increased; there is an exaggerated feeling of perspective.

On the other hand, close-ups of artists should never be attempted due to the excessive distortion of their features which will result. The angle of view, too, is so great that care must be taken to avoid shooting beyond the edges of sets, or including extraneous people or equipment in the picture.

Carefully used, however, these lenses are extremely useful. The sense of perspective and exciting movement which they make possible can lift many a sequence out of the ordinary.

Very Narrow-Angle Lenses (Angles of view below about 7 degrees.)

Individual lenses are usually designated by focal length (between 12 and 17 in.). It is not normal to use a lens with a focal length of more than 17 in. in a television studio. Much longer lenses are common on outside broadcasts, but these are discussed later. Studio zoom lenses may offer a 5 degree minimum angle.

Once again, all that can be said about these lenses is that they exaggerate the advantages and disadvantages of narrow-angle lenses. Focusing, in particular, can present terrible problems. If a close-up of a moving artist is taken with a 17 in. lens, the camera-man must concentrate very carefully to keep the subject in focus. The minimum focusing distance of a 12 in. lens is about $6\frac{1}{2}$ ft., and of a 17 in. lens, about 11 ft.—although 3 ft. to $1\frac{1}{2}$ ft. are possible with modern zooms at 5 degrees.

These long focal length lenses are heavier than the lenses which are normally mounted on a turret. They are invariably supplied, therefore, with a counterbalancing-weight, which must be mounted on the lens turret diagonally opposite the position of the long focal length lens. This counterbalancing-weight prevents the weight of the lens from disturbing the location of the turret, and from affecting the smoothness of turret rotation.

Turrets and Turret Rotation

Camerawork is influenced in many important ways by the design of the camera head and its mounting. Where camera lenses are mounted on a rotating turret, certain techniques have developed that make operation just that much quicker and quieter.

Only one lens at any time is in the taking position, and the siting of this taking lens varies from camera to camera. On some makes of camera the lens which is in the "six o'clock" position on the turret is the lens which is in use; on others it is the lens which is in the "five o'clock" position, and so on.

Lenses are sometimes screwed on to the turret, and on some makes of camera they are held in place by two retaining clips. The latter method is probably the better, since it makes for quick and easy interchanging of lenses.

On a four-lens turret, for example, there are four mounting points for the lenses, and each of these points is numbered on the front of the turret. On most modern cameras, as each numbered lens mounting is placed into the taking position, a corresponding number lights up around the periphery of the cameraman's viewfinder. The cameraman can then see at a glance which turret position is in use. If he knows which lens has been mounted at that numbered position he will know which lens is in the taking position.

For this reason lenses should always be mounted on a turret in a certain order. The most common method is to place the widest angle lens on position one, the normal lens on position two, and so on. It will then soon be a matter of instinct to connect position two, say, with a 24-degree lens, and the selection of another lens can be made accurately and swiftly.

This system of mounting the lenses so that the widest angle lens is on position one, and the narrowest angle on position four (on a four-lens turret), should be maintained when additional lenses are mounted in place of existing lenses. A cameraman soon gets into the habit of rotating the turret to a higher number when he wants to select a narrower angle lens. Any interruption of this standard sequence can lead to dangerous confusion during fast lens changes when "on the air".

The most common method of rotating the turret is by turning a handle—which is placed near the back of the camera—through 360 degrees. This rotates the turret so that the next numbered lens mounting is brought into the taking position. The handle can be turned both in a clockwise and anti-clockwise direction, so that positions one or three of the turret can be selected from position two with one swing of the lens-change handle. It follows that on a four-lens turret a cameraman should never have to turn the lens-change handle more than twice in order to select any lens.

If a cameraman turns the handle three times in these circumstances it is an indication that he has made an error of judgment. This is bad technique, and can lead to a delay of a second or two in framing his next shot. Those couple of seconds are very often vital.

There are other methods of rotating the turret; they vary from camera to camera. The cameraman must familiarize himself with the type installed on the make of camera he is operating. Turret rotation must become second nature to him, and he must learn to change to another lens as quickly as it takes him to think about it.

But he should never let his enthusiasm to become the "quickest swinger in the business" blind him to the fact that fast lens changes mean more noise. He must develop a technique whereby he can change lenses with a minimum of noise. That way he keeps everyone happy.

Some turrets are rotated electrically. The cameraman sets a pointer to the required turret position number, and the turret rotates for him. This type of turret rotation is very much slower than manual rotation, and most cameramen prefer the latter method.

The Zoom Lens

As described briefly in an earlier chapter, the zoom lens is a lens composed of multiple movable elements. These elements are so designed and linked to each other, that by moving a simple control the focal length of the lens can be progressively changed from long to short.

Most earlier studio zoom lenses suffered from the limitations of a small range of focal lengths; a typical range being 2 to 8 in. (a ratio of 4:1). This provided a similar range of focal lengths to a standard lens complement mounted on a turret. And since it is very often quicker to rotate a lens turret to a new position than it is to reset a shot on a zoom lens, the camera was a far more flexible piece of apparatus without the zoom lens.

Further, many zoom lenses project some distance in front of the camera and thereby restrict camera movement. Crabbing in particular can be a hazardous operation unless the camera is at a safe distance from the subject.

Once the zoom lens has been set up and focused on a subject, however, that subject will always remain in focus during zooming. The lens can be zoomed out to provide a wide shot, or zoomed in to a close-up. Providing neither the subject nor the camera moves, the subject will remain in focus. But refocusing will be necessary for any movement of the subject which takes him outside the depth of field of the lens.

The zoom lens provides an infinite variety of focal lengths, within its inherent range. Since these can be changed smoothly from short to long (i.e. wide-angle to narrow-angle), the camera can appear to zoom into, or out from a subject. But the effect of zooming into a subject is not the same as actually moving the camera closer.

The ratio between the size of foreground objects and background objects varies as a camera moves closer. It may be 2:1 at the beginning of the movement, and 5:1 at the end. But if the ratio is 2:1 at the beginning of a *zoom*, it is 2:1 at the end.

Zooming into a scene has the same effect as physically moving a camera closer to a photograph or painting. No amount of movement of a camera towards a photograph will alter the ratio in size between foreground and background objects on the photograph. In other words, the proportions cannot be altered by this camera movement. Zooming into a three-dimensional subject provides the same effect as moving the camera closer to a two-dimensional (flat) subject.

Thus, zooming produces an unnatural "blowing up" and "shrinking" effect, that is quite unlike the natural result that comes from camera tracking. Some directors condemned the zoom lens for this reason, but the real answer to them is "don't zoom, track as usual". The restricted angular change available disappointed others.

But then zoom lenses appeared with a range of 10:1, providing a choice of focal lengths from 1·6 to 16 inches. This gave the zoom lens new opportunities. The mechanics of zooming and focusing, too, became more sophisticated with servo control or powered zooming incorporated into some models. The shot-box, a device for setting the lens to a particular focal length at the press of a button, allowed us to select any angle between 5 and 50 degrees.

Thus, many of the objections to the use of the zoom lens in the studio were overcome, while on outside broadcasts it became almost indispensable. Adaptors are now available which can alter the focal range of the lens. A 2X adaptor, for example, converts a 1·6 to 16 in. range to a 3 to 32 in. range in a matter of minutes. A camera with a 10:1 zoom lens and a set of adaptors is a flexible instrument.

Later still, zoom lenses with a 16:1 range emerged—something cameramen could only dream about a few years ago. And with servo-assistance the lens can be zoomed in from maximum wide-shot to close-up in about a second. This is best done when the camera is not "on air", but it is an extremely useful device to help the cameraman pick out the details of an exciting and unexpected incident on an outside broadcast.

These days, then, zoom lenses are to be seen more and more in television studios. Colour cameras are invariably equipped with them. So some advice on their operation will be found in a later chapter.

On monochrome cameras, zoom lenses either replace the turret or are inserted into one of the lens mountings. The control mechanism is then mounted on a separate panning handle, and this is attached to the panning head on the opposite side to the existing panning handle. One end of a cable is then fitted to the zoom control mechanism, and the other end to the special zoom socket on the outside of the lens. A second cable is fitted, in similar manner, to operate the focus mechanism of the lens.

The cameraman then has two controls which he can operate. One operates the actual zooming of the lens, and this is usually in the form of a pivoted arm or a wheel. The other controls the focusing of the lens, and is sometimes contained in a twist grip or is governed by a wheel or capstan.

To set up the zoom lens, the following proceedure should be adopted. Zoom out as far as the lens will allow. Focus on the subject in long-shot by means of the *camera* focusing mechanism. Then zoom into the subject as tight as the lens will allow. Refocus the lens, using the *zoom* focusing mechanism. Zoom out again, and check that the long shot is still in focus. If it is not, adjust focus using the *camera* focusing mechanism.

The lens is now set for zooming into, or out from, the subject, and will stay in focus during the operation. If the subject moves, and refocusing is necessary, adjustments should be made using the *zoom* focusing mechanism.

As mentioned earlier, this setting-up operation takes much more time than swinging to another lens and refocusing. Also, a great degree of skill is often required to adjust the zoom focus while zooming is being carried out, and the cameraman will sometimes wish that he had been left with a normal complement of lenses and a trackable dolly.

Checking Lens Settings

Whenever lenses are removed for any reason, we must take a number of routine precautions. Firstly, remember fragility and cleanliness. Apart from ensuring that the lenses are remounted in the correct order on the turret, the cameraman must check that the lenses are each set at the correct "stop"—$f5 \cdot 6$, $f8$, or whatever is the current studio practice. The normal working stop does vary from one studio to another. Much depends on the type of camera in use, and level of light available.

But whether or not the lenses are mounted each morning, the stops at which each lens should be set must be checked by the cameraman before rehearsals commence. And they must always be checked again before the start of transmissions. This must become automatic on the part of the cameraman; he must never be caught with an incorrectly set lens iris.

He should familiarize himself, too, with the range of f stops available on each of the lenses he is using. Some lenses have a range of $f2 \cdot 8$ to $f22$; others, particularly the narrower angle lenses, have a range of $f4 \cdot 5$ to $f32$. These narrower angle lenses, therefore, cannot be opened up to more than $f4 \cdot 5$, and cannot be used where the level of light available requires an aperture wider than $f4 \cdot 5$.

Care of Lenses

Lenses are expensive, precision-made pieces of equipment, and television studios are by no means free from dust. Care must be taken, therefore, to keep lenses clean to ensure optimum image quality, and since some studios delegate the maintenance of lenses to cameramen, a few tips might prove useful.

It is widely held that lenses should not be cleaned and polished too often, however, and provided they are not subjected to constant attack by dirt and grease, a careful wipe every month or so should be sufficient. The lens coating is delicate and easily damaged.

76

When not in use, particularly overnight, lenses should be covered. Most lenses are supplied with caps for this purpose, but where no caps are available the camera and lenses should be covered with a dust-proof jacket. In some studios, lenses are removed from the cameras after a day's work and stowed in specially designed lens-boxes. This not only protects the lenses from dust, but also prevents them being accidentally damaged by stage-hands and lighting personnel, who might be setting their equipment overnight.

But if the lenses are handled carelessly when they are being mounted on the camera or placed in the lens-boxes, more harm than good can come from this practice.

The actual surface of the lens must never be touched by hand. A greasy stain will be left, and this is more detrimental to the lens than a layer of dust. And on no account should anything be allowed near the lens which might tend to scratch it.

Most lenses have lens-hoods attached to them. The prime purpose of these is to prevent stray light from falling on the lens and causing flare or reduced contrast. But they also contribute to keeping the lenses clean and protecting them.

Where lens-hoods are detachable—as with most long focal length lenses—they must always be placed on the lens when it is mounted on the camera turret. There are occasions when this is not possible, due to ancilliary equipment specially mounted on the front of the camera, or when the hood might be seen in a shot taken with a wide-angle lens. But apart from situations such as these, a lens-hood must be regarded as an integral part of the lens.

Before attempting to clean a lens, all loose dust must be removed with a soft lens brush. Every camera crew should have two or three lens brushes as part of their equipment. If there are none available their employers should supply them—they are an investment.

After all the dust has been carefully brushed from the surface of the lens, it can then be polished, very gently, with soft lens-issues. Any finger marks or greasy stains should be removed with a lens brush dipped in alcohol or methylated spirits.

The cameraman should look after his lenses. They are essential tools in the expression of his art. Remember, prevention is better than cure.

.T.C.—F

6

PICTURE COMPOSITION

PROBABLY more nonsense has been written about the principles of composition—both in favour of them and decrying them—than about any other aspect of camerawork. But whatever the aspiring cameraman might have read for or against the subject, he will soon learn, from personal experience behind a camera, that a knowledge of this subject is essential if he is to succeed in his profession.

Why should it be necessary to arrange the subjects of a picture to conform to certain principles? Why not point the camera in the general direction of the subject and let the viewer look for himself?

The explanation is that once a frame has been placed around a scene, it matters very much how the elements of that scene are disposed within this frame. There is a main point of interest in every picture. If the picture is not composed correctly, the eye can be led away from this centre of interest, and the value of the shot might then be minimized.

If a picture is correctly composed, it is generally found to be balanced. There are no disturbing empty spaces; the eye does not have to wander over the scene until it finds what it is supposed to be concentrating on. The picture looks right and is pictorially pleasing.

When we want to introduce a feeling of depth—or when we wish to exaggerate perspective—we must compose the picture according to certain rules if we are to achieve the desired effect. And by applying the principles of composition we can impart vitality, atmosphere, formality, even excitement to a picture.

Composition can be defined as the art of arranging the elements of a picture in such a way that the viewer's attention is concentrated on the centre of interest. It will inevitably follow that the picture will be pictorially pleasing. But too many people make the mistake of placing this last consideration first. By sticking too losely to the rules, and becoming obsessed by the principles of he subject, a cameraman can make a meticulous nuisance of imself.

The television cameraman, with little time to select and adjust shots, must develop an instinctive feeling for composition. When he is operating a camera on a major television show (a play for instance) he might be required to shoot something like two hundred shots during the course of the programme. And in many cases he will have only half a dozen seconds in which to compose his shots.

Not for him the advantages of the stills' photographers, or even the film cameramen. They can spend minutes, sometimes hours, perfecting their shots, and in many cases if these are not satisfactory they can be retaken. This is not to decry the skills of such cameramen. They have a different type of job to do, and their standards are usually higher.

But the television cameraman must compose instantly and instinctively. And since his shots will follow and precede shots taken by other cameramen, there is a basis for comparison between them. If one cameraman is guilty of bad composition, his work will stand out like a sore thumb. And even if the viewer is not aware of the niceties of composition, there will be something vaguely disturbing in his viewing.

Pictorial composition is important, then. And the television cameraman must fully understand the principles of the subject.

Visual Elements of a Scene

The visual elements which make up a scene can be divided into the following: mass (artists, props, furniture, etc.); line (actual lines in the scene, grouping of people, direction of movement); tone (the displacement of the range of tones from white to black); and depth (the actual or apparent depth of the scene, in which the principles of perspective illusion play a major part).

The cameraman can control some of these elements by his choice of lenses, the position and height of his camera, and by suggestions for the placing of subjects.

The set designer, too, can exert a strong influence on the visual appearance of a scene. He can contribute to the effective composition of a picture by the size, shape, relative position, and tone of his sets. In particular, he can apply his skill to create a feeling of depth and perspective illusion to a scene. He should be as well versed in the art of composition as the cameraman.

Some of the elements of a picture are controllable by the

lighting director, and in some cases successful composition can result from lighting techniques alone. But lighting is normally employed to augment the disposition of other elements of a scene. This is achieved by the distribution of highlights and shadows, and by the introduction of special lighting effects of varying shapes, sizes, and tonal values.

Mass

A picture rarely contains one element of mass only. Even the simple shot of a news reader will contain the artist, a desk, a set in the background, and perhaps a station symbol mounted on the set. The more elements of mass there are in a picture, the more complex will be the problem of arranging them to provide a well-composed shot.

Since the television picture is comparatively small, it is better to keep the detail in a scene down to the minimum than to clutter up the frame with a confusion of detail. A mass of small detail in a picture will not register in a wide shot, and will not be seen in a close-up.

However, these elements of mass must be arranged in the shot to provide a pleasing, balanced picture, and the centre of interest must be well defined.

If artists and objects are framed symmetrically, the resulting picture is rarely satisfactory. The effect is too formal. The shot is visually uninteresting, and there is no obvious centre of interest. In most cases a slight alteration of the position of the camera—or the subject—is all that is necessary to destroy this unwanted symmetry. And if these readjustments follow the principles we shall be discussing, a pleasing picture with a well-defined centre of interest will result.

Fig. 15. *Left:* A too-symmetrical design; the three elements of mass are in line. *Right.* A slight readjustment of two elements presents a less symmetrical, but well-balanced layout.

80

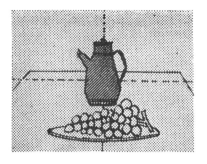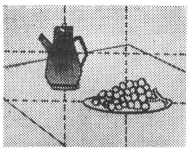

Fig. 16. *Left:* This is not good composition. The two objects are in the centre of the picture and do not hold our interest. *Right:* This is better. The cameraman has moved his camera to the left, and placed the subjects on the intersection of thirds.

The geometric centre of the picture is not the best place for the centre of interest. It is difficult to explain why this is so, but it is a fact. If the picture is divided into thirds, however, both horizontally and vertically, the points of intersection are the areas most suitable for the placing of points of interest. This principle of "intersection of thirds", as it is called, stands up very well in practice, particularly if the other elements in the shot are arranged so that they lead the eye towards these points. This system of placing points of interest on the intersection of thirds is particularly useful when framing two-shots and over-the-shoulder shots, which we shall look at in greater detail in the next chapter.

It might be worth mentioning here that this principle is related to the theory of the "Golden Mean", known to the ancient Greeks. They maintained that centres of interest should be placed five-eighths of the distance in from any of the edges of the frame.

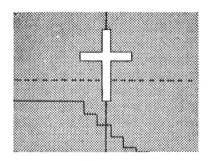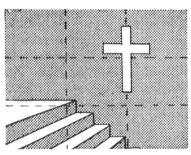

Fig. 17. *Left:* Not very good. The cross is in the centre and it has not been balanced in relation to the steps. *Right:* A vast improvement. The camera has been moved to the right, the cross placed near the intersection of thirds, and the lines of the foreground steps lead our eyes to the centre of interest.

81

These have been proved to be strong accent points, and the technique is well known to painters and others.

For all practical purposes five-eighths is almost two thirds—which is relatively easy for the cameraman to calculate. Since he must frame his shots within a short space of time, the principle of intersection of thirds is entirely suited to his needs.

Triangulation

This is probably the best-known method of composition. If the centre of interest lies at the apex of a triangle having its base at the bottom of the frame, a stable composition with a well-defined centre of interest will result. This does not mean, of course, that subjects should be arranged to form a definite pyramid. The principle should be applied in more subtle ways than that. But if

Fig. 18. *Left:* The subjects are badly placed. The centre of interest—the woman—does not hold our attention. *Right:* The man has been repositioned, and a nicely balanced, triangular composition is the result.

the general arrangement of the picture elements suggest a triangular formation, the picture will have a solid, balanced composition.

A close-up of an artist, including his shoulders, has a suggestion of triangulation about it. The shoulders form the base of the triangle, and the centre of interest, the face, rests on this base in a pleasantly stable manner. Triangular composition is even more obvious if the shot includes the artist's elbows, which are resting on a desk.

The important point is that the centre of interest must be supported by the other elements of the scene. The simplest method, and often the most effective, is to provide it with a base which it can rest on, and so form a roughly triangular composition.

Fig. 19. *Left:* There is a suggestion of triangulation even in this simple shot. *Right:* This is stronger triangulation. The position of the arms leads our eyes inevitably to the subject's face.

Line

When we talk of line in a picture we can mean the actual lines which are inherent in the scene; the grouping of objects, artists, and sets; or the direction of movement within the frame. But however line is introduced into a scene, its form and direction are important. Line can convey a real sense of atmosphere and mood to a scene, and can add significance to the centre of interest by leading the eye inexorably towards it.

Lines which run parallel to the frame of a picture—that is, vertically and horizontally—give a feeling of formality, neatness, and dependability. The picture is unlikely to be exciting, but excitement is not the aim when a picture is composed with lines such as these.

If horizontal and vertical lines are deliberately overdominant in a scene, they can help create a harsh, uncompromising, soulless atmosphere. Think of a shot of a prison interior. The picture is dominated by straight horizontal and vertical lines—dozens of them. The effect is grim and monotonous; and so it should be.

Straight parallel lines, therefore, should be used with discretion. It is all too easy for the effect of formality and neatness to be over-done.

If the dominant lines in a picture are set at an angle to the sides of the frame, a sense of vitality, vigour, and even excitement can result. The orderly neatness of lines parallel to the sides of frame can easily become boring and lifeless, as we have seen.

A close-up of an artist with his head tilted a little to one side is usually more attractive than a square-on shot. A shot taken at right-angles to a row of houses has nothing like the life and

Fig. 20. *Left:* A well-composed, simple picture. *Right:* Rotating the shoulders slightly and tilting the head, however, has introduced diagonal lines into the shot. The subject has been given "life".

interest of a shot taken at a diagonal angle to it. In most cases, a slight movement of the camera is often all that is necessary to convert dull horizontal and vertical lines into exciting diagonal ones.

But if the diagonal lines are overdominant they can create an effect that is confusing. This is all very well when that kind of atmosphere is intended. But if it is not, care must be taken to prevent diagonal lines dominating a scene.

When we want to convey a feeling of gentleness, tranquillity, or softness to a scene, the dominant lines should be curved. A typical example of this type of composition is a picture of a rolling landscape.

But interior shots, too, must contain their share of rounded lines if the right effect is to be achieved. Compare a shot of a

Fig. 21. *Left:* This square-on shot of the houses is dominated by lines parallel to the sides of the frame. It is relatively uninteresting, and gives no sense of depth. *Right:* Moving the camera to one side produces exciting diagonal lines, and adds a sense of perspective to the scene.

84

Fig. 22. Diagonal lines are over-dominant, and the shot is confusing with no obvious centre of interest.

prison cell, with its hard uncompromising lines, to a picture of a ladies' nineteenth-century bedroom, with its straight lines broken by flowing curves. Admittedly the set-dressings accentuate the difference, but they really ensure the correct use of line in the picture.

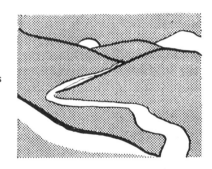

Fig. 23. Curved lines suggest gentleness and tranquillity.

If the roundness of line is overdone the effect can be weak and overeffeminate.

The cameraman has little control over this form of line in a picture, unless line is achieved by the grouping of objects and artists. But he can contribute to the success of this form of

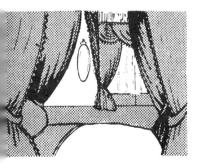

Fig. 24. The over-dominant rounded lines suggest femininity and graciousness. They are ideal, therefore, for this shot of a ladies' nineteenth-century bedroom.

85

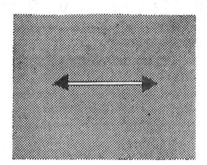

Fig. 25. Movement directly across the screen is uninteresting.

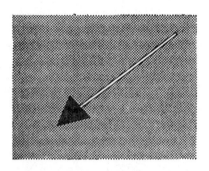

It is far more exciting if it is diagonal

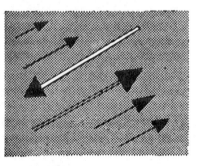

. . . particularly if it opposes the general direction of movement in the scene.

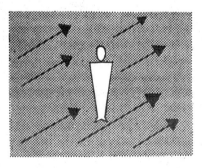

Our interest is held by the only static part of a moving scene.

composition by excluding unwanted straight lines from his shots, and by paying careful attention to the height of his camera.

By raising or lowering his camera dolly he can often include or exclude certain aspects of a scene. He must give some thought, too, to the angle at which he is shooting the scene. If he shoots at an acute angle to a set he can convert rounded lines into diagonals, and the effect will be ruined.

Movement

Movement across a picture is closely related to the subject of line in composition. Together with the careful use of sound, movement within a scene is the most dramatic means of drawing attention to the subject which is the centre of interest.

The most effective direction of movement across a scene is diagonal. This principle agrees with the maxim that diagonal lines in a shot are more exciting than horizontal or verticals. Artist movement across a scene, and parallel to the bottom of frame, is generally uninteresting. The apparent size of the artist does not vary—since he is moving parallel to the camera—and there is little in the movement to heighten the interest of the viewer.

Artist movement directly towards the camera can sometimes be effective, particularly if a fast, dramatic change in size of the subject is wanted. In a very short space of time an artist can come from the background to dominate the scene, and the effect can be quite startling if the method is used intelligently.

But for all general purposes it will be found that diagonal movement is the most interesting. This is particularly so when shooting ballet, for example. But normal movement of artists during television plays, or musical shows, will be given that something extra if it is diagonal.

There are two basic methods of using movement to emphasize the main subject in a picture.

1. By contrasting the subject's movement with the general direction of movement within the scene. Think of a shot in which a large crowd of people are moving across the scene towards the right-hand side of the picture. If one person is pushing his way through them towards the left of frame, interest will immediately be centred on him.

If he is running towards left of frame, and people around him are running towards the right of frame, not only will he be the centre of interest in the picture, but the speed of his movement will be exaggerated. The effect will be exciting.

87

2. By making the main subject the only static part of a moving scene, or the only moving part of a static scene. Imagine again the crowd of people moving towards the right-hand side of frame. A little boy sitting on the floor and crying would immediately command our interest.

In the same way, imagine a battleground littered with motionless bodies. Suddenly one of them stirs and tries to rise. Obviously our interest will be directed at this movement.

These are simple, obvious examples, but the principle should not be forgotten. It can be applied in far more subtle ways, and the effect will be worthwhile.

Tone

In black-and-white television pictures the various colours of a scene are reproduced as varying shades of grey, with white at one end of the scale and black at the other. The arrangement of these tones in a picture is part of the art of composition.

Even if the elements of line and mass in a scene lead the eye towards the centre of interest, the effect can be marred if the disposition of the elements of tone is not considered. A highlight to one side of the main subject, for example, can distract the viewer's attention away from this centre of interest.

The cameraman has very little control over the range of tones available in any shot he may take. This tonal range falls within the responsibility of the set designer, who can vary the range by careful use of materials and colours, and of the lighting director, who varies the intensity and distribution of light. In colour TV, there is the additional problem of achieving simultaneously good

Fig. 26. The position of the subjects in both shots is identical, but the disposition of the highlights has changed the centre of interest from the dog (left) to the man (right).

88

Fig. 27. The centre of interest is the brightest part of the picture and contrasts vividly with the other tones. He cannot fail to claim our attention.

separation in the grey scale for black-and-white and good colour balance for the colour version.

But there are certain principles which can help the cameraman to compose his pictures successfully with the tonal range at his disposal.

The centre of interest should be placed, whenever possible, in the brightest part of the scene, or it should contain the greatest tonal contrast in the picture.

Comparatively bright patches near the corners of frame should be avoided. They tend to lead the eye away from the scene, and the main point of interest might become less significant. The composition will be more compact if the corners of the frame are a little darker than the main scene. The eye naturally tends, then, to concentrate on the important areas of the picture.

If the darker tones of a scene can be arranged near the base of the frame, the result will be to provide a stable support for the centre of interest. The main subject will sit quite naturally on this

Fig. 28. Left: The elements of the scene have been carefully framed to produce a well-composed shot. But the highlights near the edges of the frame distract attention from the main subjects. Right: This is a vast improvement. Our eyes are drawn to the centre of interest and the shot is pleasingly compact.

89

Fig. 29. The darker tones near the bottom of the frame have provided an ideal base for this triangular composition.

darker base, and this arrangement links up well with any attempt at triangulation in composition.

In colour TV we have the further problem of ensuring that background colours do not clash too markedly—except for intended effect—when intercutting on the same scene or in transition from an establishing shot. Although, remember, the cameraman himself sees only a monochrome picture in his view-finder.

Depth

The TV picture is inherently flat. The majority of pictures are of three-dimensional subjects, and most of the skills of the various people engaged in this profession are directed towards the creation of a three-dimensional effect—an illusion of perspective in fact.

. The illusions of solidity, space and depth are achieved by arranging the elements of a scene in such a way that they add a feeling of depth to a two-dimensional picture. There are four basic methods of achieving this.

1. *Perspective of Mass*

The elements of mass in a scene can be arranged to create a sense of depth. In some cases perspective illusion can be exaggerated, and a false sense of spaciousness conveyed to the viewer. This is very necessary in television where studio space precludes the use of vast sets, and other means have to be employed to create this sense of depth.

The cameraman must grasp the principles of perspective of mass, since he is mainly responsible for the successful application of this method. The position of his camera; the lens to be used for each shot; the height of his camera; all are important.

Let us examine this subject of perspective illusion from the

90

beginning. Imagine a picture of two men, one standing closer to the camera than the other. If the man in foreground appears very large and the man in background very small, the eye and brain will interpret this as indicating that they are a great distance apart.

In fact they might be standing much closer to each other than the picture suggests. As we shall see later, we can create this effect by using a wide-angle lens. But the point is that the viewer will be guided by the interpretation of his eyes and brain. The eyes and brain can be misled, however, and it is the cameraman's job to do just this.

Again, imagine a shot of a singer standing in front of a background depicting a woodland scene. There will be little sense of depth in the picture. But if we add a foreground piece—say the trunk and overhanging limb of a tree—the artist will be viewed in relation to this extra plane, in addition to the background. Depending on the relative, apparent sizes of these elements of the scene, a corresponding feeling of depth will be added to the picture.

What can the cameraman do to assist the illusion of depth?

As we saw in the chapter on lenses, wide-angle lenses provide a greater difference in size between foreground and background subjects than narrow-angle lenses, and they should be used whenever perspective illusion is required.

But changing to a wide-angle lens will not necessarily add a feeling of perspective to a shot. There is a basic rule which must not be forgotten when considering this subject. *There is no change in perspective, between one lens and another, if the camera position is unchanged.*

We can understand this better if we look at an example. The same two men are standing in our scene, one closer to the camera than the other. Using an intermediate lens, the shot is framed so that the foreground man's feet are near the bottom of frame, and his head is about one-fifth of the vertical height of the shot below the top of frame. Obviously, the background man will appear to be much smaller. Let us say for the sake of this example that the ratio between the size of the foreground man and the size of the background man is 2:1—i.e. the foreground man appears to be twice the size of the other.

Let us imagine that we now change lenses, and shoot the scene with a wide-angle lens—say one with an angle of view of 35 degrees —but do not move the camera. We shall be seeing very much more of the scene, and our two men will be appreciably smaller. *But the ratio in size between them will still be 2:1.* There will have been

Fig. 30. This shot was taken with an intermediate lens. The ratio between the sizes of the foreground and background men is 2 : 1.

The camera has not been moved but the shot has been taken with a lens having a wider angle of view. Both men appear smaller, but the ratio in size between them is still 2 : 1. There is no change in perspective.

The camera has been moved closer—still using the wide angle lens. The foreground man is now the same size as he was in the top figure, but the background man is very much smaller. The ratio in size between them is 4 : 1. There is a greater sense of perspective in the bottom figure. This is because we changed to a wider lens *and* moved the camera closer to the scene.

no increase in perspective through changing to the wider lens: the foreground man will still appear to be twice the size of the background man.

However, if we move the camera closer (still using the wide-angle lens) until we frame the foreground man exactly as we did in the first example—feet at the bottom of frame, etc.—there will be quite a difference between the two shots. The background man will now appear to be very much smaller than he was when the intermediate lens was used; in fact the ratio in size between the two men might be something like 4:1. The eye interprets this as indicating that the men are very far apart.

92

We have created an illusion of distance which was not there when the narrower angle lens was used. But remember, we achieved this by changing to a wider lens *and* moving the camera closer, until the foreground man was framed as in the first example. Merely changing to a wider lens did not alter the perspective of the scene one iota.

It is this maxim which explains the unreal quality of the zoom lens. As the zoom lens is zoomed out, its effective angle of view is increased. But there is no change of camera position. The ratio in size between the subjects in the scene will be the same at the end of the zoom as it was at the beginning. The eye is not accustomed to this effect. As we move away from a scene we expect the ratio in size between the various elements of that scene to be constantly changing. Moving the camera provides this sensation: zooming does not.

We can exaggerate perspective of mass, then, by the use of wide-angle lenses, and by moving the camera closer to a scene to obtain the same image size. But the height of the camera is important too.

High shots, when they are taken with wide-angle lenses, fore-shorten vertical objects, and increase the feeling of height. Horizontal planes are emphasized, foreground objects are less dominant, and maximum use is made of floor area.

Low shots, with wide-angle lenses, tend to emphasize foreground objects and vertical planes, and provide unusual, dramatic viewpoints.

The cameraman should always be on the lookout for methods of utilizing the properties of lenses (and the effect of varying camera positions) in the art of adding depth in a scene.

2. *Perspective of Line*

This consists of arranging the line in a scene, not merely to provide an interesting composition, but to increase the sense of perspective illusion.

The set designer is the person who can contribute most to this method, and some of the devices used by him are works of mathematical art. Sets are sometimes constructed so that those pieces of scenery farthest from camera are much smaller than corresponding pieces in foreground. This helps to exaggerate perspective, and the set looks much bigger than it really is, particularly if wide-angle lenses are used—as they should be.

Sometimes the lines on the floor of the set will be matched to lines on a backcloth, so that they merge into each other.

But whenever the set designer has designed his sets with perspective illusion in mind, the cameraman must shoot these scenes from the correct angle if the effect is not to be lost. The cameraman will soon learn by experience where he should place his camera to utilize sets which have been designed in this way. If he is in any doubt, he should consult the designer or the director.

Even when shooting ordinary sets, however, the cameraman should try to avoid a frontal approach. By moving his camera position a little to one side, diagonal lines will appear in his shot, and this will contribute to the illusion of perspective.

3. *Perspective of Tone*

A feeling of depth will be given to scenes if the tones are so arranged that the darkest areas are in foreground and the lightest in background.

The set designer and the lighting director are the people who can provide this set of circumstances. But the cameraman can often utilize existing conditions to provide the effect needed.

4. *Differential Focus*

This has been mentioned in the chapter on lenses. If a lens with a narrow depth of field—such as a narrow-angle lens, or any lens which has been "opened up" to a wide aperture ($f1 \cdot 9$, $f2 \cdot 8$)—is focused on a subject, the background will almost certainly fall outside the depth of field and be out of focus. The main subject will then stand out in sharp relief, and this adds depth to the shot.

Lenses can be opened up to provide this effect only if the light level is not too high. Since most lighting is planned for a relatively steady level throughout a programme, this method of differential focus is usually accomplished with narrow-angle lenses.

Apart from adding depth to the shot, differential focus helps to concentrate the viewer's attention on the main subject. It is an extremely useful device for the cameraman to have at his fingertips.

Summing Up

This subject of the principles of composition is so important that it might be as well to sum up all that has been discussed.

Composition is the art of arranging the elements of a scene (mass, line, tone, depth) to emphasize the centre of interest.

The aim of the cameraman should be to balance the picture so that the eye is led inevitably to the main subject of his shot. There should be no vacant spaces, or distracting detail, to entice the eye away.

The shot must be balanced, but symmetry should be avoided.

Placing the main subject on the intersection of thirds, or at the apex of a triangular composition, are well-proven methods of achieving the aims of composition.

Pictorial composition must become instinctive. There is little time during transmissions to experiment with the disposition of the elements of a scene.

Lines which run parallel to the edges of frame present a formal, neat composition, but are not as interesting as diagonal lines. Smooth, flowing curves in a scene suggest tranquillity and softness.

Diagonal movement across a scene is usually more interesting than horizontal or vertical movement.

Movement is more significant if it contrasts with other movement in the scene, or if the other subjects in the scene are static.

The centre of interest should contain the highlights of a scene, or provide the greatest tonal contrast.

A dark tone at the bottom of frame provides a suitable base on which to rest the centre of interest.

The corners of a shot should be, ideally, darker than the rest of the scene, so that the eye will concentrate on the scene itself.

Those engaged in television are continually striving to add perspective illusion to this two-dimensional medium.

The four basic methods of achieving this are (1) perspective of mass, (2) perspective of line, (3) perspective of tone, and (4) differential focus. The cameraman is concerned in all these methods.

A greater sense of depth is imparted with wide-angle lenses than with narrow-angle lenses. But there is no change in perspective unless there is a change of camera position, whatever lens is used.

Perspective sets must be shot from the correct angle or the effect will be ruined.

Pictorial composition is important, whatever the cynics may say. In television it is particularly important, not only because the cameraman must develop it as an instinct, but because his shots are seen in immediate relation to shots taken by other cameramen.

7

FRAMING TECHNIQUE

In the previous chapter we looked at the basic principles of composition, and we can now consider their practical application in the television studio.

The terminology used to identify the various shots in current use has become fairly standardized throughout the industry. There are, however, certain slight differences in opinion between one studio and another. What one would call a medium close-up, the other might call a tight mid-shot. These differences are not as important as they might appear, since the end product will invariably be the same in each case—and that is what matters.

A few of the terms used in this chapter, therefore, might differ slightly from those used by some of the readers. But every effort has been made to adhere to the terminology which is most popular in British television.

Framing Artists

The television cameraman will find that the majority of his shots will include people. And the correct method of framing these artists is something he must learn as soon as possible—and then never forget.

He must consider this question of correct artist framing from two viewpoints—his own, and that of the boom operator. In the first place he must learn the right and wrong methods of framing. Then he must appreciate the limitations placed on him by the boom operator and the extent to which he must compromise his artistic desires with the practical requirements of television.

The viewer must hear as well as see, and the sound is as important as the picture. But it is not more important. The cameraman must never compromise below the point of acceptable composition. There must be give and take on both sides.

Because of this need for sound coverage, a fairly universal

standard has evolved over the years which dictates the acceptable amount of headroom on any given shot. Headroom is the amount of space between the top of the artist's head and the top of frame.

It is generally less than the cameraman likes to allow, and more than the boom operator likes to concede: it has become a matter of compromise. But the good cameraman should be capable of always allowing the same amount of headroom each time he frames a close-up, for example.

Also, since one cameraman's shots will be seen in relation to the shots taken by his colleagues, every cameraman must allow the same amount of headroom for each type of shot. This does not mean that the headroom allowed on a close-up should be the same as that allowed on a long shot—far from it. But close-up must match close-up, and long shot must match long shot.

There is one more problem the cameraman must consider. The home viewer will not receive the exact area of picture that the cameraman sees in his viewfinder. Some detail around the edges of his pictures will never reach the viewer, for some viewfinders are deliberately designed to reveal subjects on the edge of his shot. Furthermore, most home receivers mask-off their picture borders.

The greatest cut-off will be evident at the top of frame, and what the cameraman thinks is perfect headroom on his viewfinder picture will probably be too little by the time the viewer sees it.

It is rather difficult to advise the cameraman on the amount by which he should increase his headroom in order to allow for this loss during transmission. It is something he should study for himself, and devise his own method for calculating the correct adjustment to his shots. The difference is not great, but it is there and it must be allowed for.

To avoid confusion, the diagrams throughout this book show the picture areas which the viewer should receive, and the cameraman must adjust his framing in the studio to provide this end product.

Positioning the Eyes

Before going on to examples of picture framing, there is one point which must be mentioned. So far as television is concerned, eyes are the most important features of the human subject. Apart from the fact that they must always be sharply in focus, their position in the frame has a direct bearing on the headroom allowed.

Eyes should never be placed exactly half-way up the frame. This is the basic rule, and it is varied only in very long shots, or when there is a false top of frame (which we shall discuss later). The human eyes are situated about half-way up the head—to many people's surprise—and placing them on the centre line of a shot (a poor position for the centre of interest) normally leads to excessive headroom.

Some cameramen are convinced that the best position for the eyes is exactly two-thirds of the distance up the frame. But this is too inflexible a rule. There are very few occasions when this framing would be correct. For all normal shots, it can be said that eyes should never be placed as low as the centre line of the picture, and never higher than two-thirds of the distance up the frame.

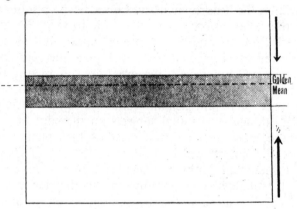

Fig. 31. Eyes should be placed in the area of the screen shown here as a shaded band. Its lower limit is half-way up the frame, and its upper limit is one-third of the distance down from the top of the frame. It can be seen that the Greek "Golden Mean" runs through this band.

The cameraman should imagine a horizontal band running across his frame. The bottom of this band will be the horizontal line which bisects the frame, and its upper limit will be a horizontal line one-third of the distance down from the top of frame. Eyes must normally be placed in this band for all shots up to and including long shots.

Headroom will then automatically take care of itself. Further, the eyes will be near the Greek "Golden Mean", which was mentioned in the previous chapter. The principle of placing the eyes within this band has been found to be correct in practice so many times that the cameraman must regard it almost as a law.

If the rule does nothing else, it standardizes shots between one cameraman and another—so important in television, as we have said many times before. But it really does more than that. It ensures that eyes are placed where they should be—at a strong accent point in a frame. Eyes are all important: the cameraman must remember that when framing his shots.

But—and there is always a but—this rule does not apply once an artist is framed in anything wider than a long shot. In fact we can say that once we can see an artist's feet—and have framed him correctly—the position of the eyes in frame is no longer important. Widening the shot entails taking into consideration such other matters as footroom and foreground and background subjects. Different rules apply—the shot is no longer a portrait.

As long as the cameraman can see the artist's eyes, however, he must always focus on them. They are the natural points of interest to the viewer; they are the most dramatic means of expression; the main clues to sincerity. Out-of-focus eyes can deprive a shot of "life".

The Big Close-Up (B.C.U.)

Obviously, the point of this shot is to direct the viewer's attention at the face. It is used when the features or expression of the subject are dramatically important, and when the director wants the viewer to concentrate on them to the exclusion of anything else.

From the cameraman's point of view, the most important rule to remember is this: when a shot is so "tight" that some portion of the head must be excluded, then it is the top of the head which must be "cut off".

It is bad framing to include the top of the head and exclude the mouth. Apart from the fact that the eyes would be in the wrong position in the shot, the exclusion of the artist's mouth would disturb the viewer. He must see this feature, in addition to the eyes, if he is to experience the full effect of the B.C.U.

The Close-Up (C.U.)

The examples given for each of these shots will probably convey more than a hundred words, but some points can be mentioned.

Allowing the correct amount of headroom should not be any problem if the eyes are placed within the band we referred to earlier. This should ensure that the top of the head will be very near the top of frame, and the bottom of frame will then be roughly at the spot where the points of a man's collar would be. But do not run the bottom of frame through the artist's throat— the head must have something to stand on.

99

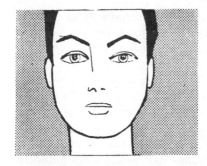

Fig. 32. *Top left:* The Big Close-Up (B.C.U.)
Above: The Close-Up (C.U.)
Left: The Medium Close-Up (M.C.U.)

More often than not, these close shots will be taken with narrow-angle lenses, and this invariably means little depth of field. The cameraman must be particularly careful to keep the lens focused on the eyes. Very little movement by the artist can take his eyes outside the depth of field, and the cameraman can guarantee to "hold focus" only if he concentrates on his work.

Incidentally, there are some terms commonly used by cameramen when referring to focusing, and we can mention them briefly here.

Let us imagine that a cameraman is taking a shot of a soldier who is standing in front of his sentry-box. To add depth to our shot, we include a tree in the foreground.

If the cameraman focuses his lens on the sentry—who must be the centre of interest—we regard the shot as being properly in focus.

But if the sentry-box is "sharp", we say that the cameraman has "focused back", and he must "focus forward" to correct this error. These terms would be reversed if the cameraman had focused on the tree.

We use the term "focusing forward", then, to describe the transference of sharp focus to a point nearer the camera than

100

before. If an artist walks towards the camera, for example, the cameraman would "focus forward" throughout the movement.

The techniques of focusing are described in greater detail in the chapter which deals with tracking. Holding focus during artist or camera movement is one of the most difficult aspects of television camerawork.

It is sometimes rather difficult to focus on some people's eyes. Although they may appear attractive on the screen, they always look unsharp if closely scrutinized.

The forehead—which is only a little nearer the camera than the eyes—can normally be relied upon to provide some lines to aid focusing. The front part of the artist's hair is another useful focusing aid, as are the ears.

If the cameraman is still having difficulty, there is usually some feature of clothing which will help him. Striped shirts and ties, small check patterns, straw hats—all these are useful focusing aids. But the cameraman must remember that the eyes are still the main point of interest—and of focus.

If the other parts of the shot which are used to help him find focus are not the same distance from the camera as the eyes, then he must move focus on to the eyes once he has satisfied himself that his picture is "sharp" on the feature he has selected. This is not quite so important in wide shots, but can be vital in close-ups where the depth of field can be very small indeed.

The Medium Close-Up (M.C.U.)

Here, with the eyes placed once again in our imaginary band, headroom will be a little greater than our previous shot—the C.U. The bottom of frame will probably run just beneath the breast-pocket of a man's suit; but this is mentioned merely as a guide.

The Mid-Shot (M.S.)

In this shot the bottom of frame will cut a standing man somewhere near his waist, and more headroom will be allowed than for the M.C.U.

If the artist is sitting, the bottom of frame should cut the arms of a normal easy chair. This is the standard "interview" shot which can be seen dozens of times in the course of regular viewing.

The Medium Long Shot (M.L.S.)

This is sometimes called the "three-quarter shot", and this gives a good indication of the framing. Headroom continues to increase

Fig. 33. *Left:* The standing Medium Shot (M.S.). *Right:* The sitting M.S.

as the shots become wider, and bottom of frame runs about the level of the artist's knees. But remember that the eyes are still all-important—they must be placed in the optimum region (Fig. 31).

As the cameraman widens his shots, he will see more and more of the settings, props., and other elements of the scene. And these must be taken into consideration when he is deciding on his composition.

The Long Shot (L.S.)

The whole of the artist's body is included in this shot. Head-room will be increased, and there must be a space between the artist's feet and bottom of frame. *But there must always be less footroom than headroom.* If they are equal, the artist will appear to be suspended in the shot. If more footroom than headroom is allowed, the shot will be unbalanced. Twice as much headroom as footroom is a good rule in practice.

These points only apply, of course, when we are considering a shot of an artist who is not standing on, or under anything. Naturally, a long shot of an artist who is standing on a rock will contain more footroom than headroom.

It must be remembered, too, that any strong projection above an artist's head will become the new, artificial top of frame, and. headroom must be judged in relation to it. When composing a long shot of an artist standing under an archway, for example, the headroom must be calculated from the artist's head to the bottom edge of the arch.

Wherever possible the bottom of frame should not cut off the artist's ankles. The artist's feet should be included in shot, with a space beneath to give him something to stand on. But when it is absolutely unavoidable that either headroom or footroom must be reduced, then it is better to reduce the footroom.

102

Fig. 34. The Medium Long Shot (M.L.S.)

The Long Shot (L.S.) *Note:* (*a*) twice as much headroom as footroom, (*b*) position of eyes no longer so important.

More footroom than headroom—but this is necessary because the artist is standing on a rostrum.

The under-side of the arch is our new artificial top of frame. Footroom and headroom have been calculated in relation to it and not to the actual top of frame.

The Very Long Shot (V.L.S.)

Here the position of the artist in frame depends very much on the other elements in the scene, and on the height of the camera. The amount and position of foreground and background dressings, the height of background sets, the tonal value of the floor—all these considerations, and many others, govern the best framing of an artist in this type of shot.

If the director has indicated that he wants more floor than background set in the shot, a high camera position should be used. If he wants the minimum of floor area in the shot, a low camera position is obviously the answer.

Very long shots provide the cameraman with the best opportunities to put into practice the principles of artistic composition. The wider the shot, the more elements of a scene will be included. If he experiments with different lenses, various camera positions and heights, and encourages the rearrangement of the artists, props., and small pieces of scenery, the cameraman can modify the pictorial value of these very long shots.

The difficulty with this type of shot, so far as the cameraman is concerned, is the need to compromise his desire to present a well-composed shot with the boom operator's keenness to place the microphone near the artist. Where the microphone *must* be placed near an artist, the cameraman must make the best of an unfortunate situation. He can frame foreground settings in such a way that they occupy the lower half of his shot, and then place the artist near the top of frame. In many cases these foreground pieces will help to add depth to the shot.

Long shots suggest "distant" sound, however, and more often than not there will be no need to place the boom microphone close to the artist in these circumstances. Sound balancers refer to this practice as keeping the "sound perspective" correct for the type

Fig. 35. The Very Long Shot (V.L.S.)

Fig. 36. The foreground objects have been cleverly framed to enable the artist to be placed near the top of frame in a natural manner. This type of framing is ideal when the artist is a singer and the boom microphone must be placed near him.

of shot. This suits the cameraman who has greater freedom to frame his long shots as they should be framed.

But the principle does not apply when he is shooting singers. The viewer still expects to hear the artist clearly even in very long shots—he does not want "perspective sound". And neither does the sound balancer, who is further concerned with the problem of keeping the artist audible in spite of the necessary background of instrumental accompaniment.

He must have his microphone close to the artist in this situation, therefore, and the cameraman can help by using foreground objects as a false base to his shots, thereby reducing the amount of headroom.

Two-Shots to Group Shots

A shot which includes two people is called a two-shot; one which includes four people is called a four-shot; and when it is intended to include a number of people—say more than six—the shot is usually referred to as a group shot.

The most unattractive two-shot is one in which the two artists are shoulder to shoulder and facing the camera. The composition is symmetrical and uninteresting, and the two artists command the same amount of attention.

That type of shot is rarely required, since the artists in a two-shot are normally talking to each other. In this case they should be placed so that they are facing each other, if only slightly. This will improve even the square-on shot.

But if one camera can shoot the artists from a little to one side, the shot will gain interest. From this position we shall see more of one artist's face than the other, and this type of shot is normally called "a two-shot favouring artist A". If another camera is then placed so that it can offer a two-shot favouring artist B, the director

105

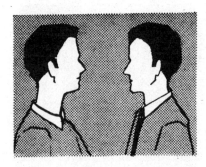

Fig. 37. *Left:* Although the artists are correctly placed in the frame, the shot lacks interest.

A camera has been placed on each side of the square-on position. They each shoot favouring two-shots which can be pleasantly intercut.

can intercut between these two cameras as the respective artists speak.

Incidentally, the cameraman must avoid "loose" framing when he is shooting more than one artist. By this we mean that a shot is neater if there are no wide gaps between the outside artists and the sides of the shot. The cameraman must frame his shots to avoid these gaps, even if this entails moving the artists closer to each other to enable the camera to be tracked nearer to them.

The most interesting type of two-shot is undoubtedly the "over-the-shoulder two-shot" (or O/S 2-shot). For this type of framing the camera should be placed so that the near artist has his back towards it, and the far artist is seen in relation to the foreground man's shoulder. These shots can be mid-shots or close-ups. But however "tight" the shot, the artist who is facing the camera should be placed as near as possible on the intersection of thirds.

If we tighten the shot so that we can see only part of the back of the head, some of the face, and a little of the shoulder of the near artist, *the shot will usually only look right if we include the ear of*

106

Fig. 38. *Left:* This is a well-composed O/S. 2-shot. *Right:* The camera has moved in but the ear of the near artist must still be included in the shot for it to be acceptable.

this near artist. Tightening the shot so that we see part of the face only is bad composition. The shot will look like a mistake; we shall lose a sense of location. If we cannot include the near artist's ear, it is far better to exclude him altogether and make the shot a close-up of the far artist.

When two cameras are shooting O/S 2-shots, each favouring alternate artists, it is imperative that both shots should be carefully matched. The cameras must shoot the artists from the same angle. Both cameras must normally be at the same height and the same type of lens used on each. If one camera is higher than the other, undue prominence and dramatic effect will be given to one artist when the shots are intercut. If one camera is using a lens with a wider angle of view than the other camera, the artists might appear to be farther apart on one shot than on the other.

These points must always be borne in mind whenever two or more cameras are meant to match their shots to each other.

When shooting three-shots, group shots, and so on, the grouping of artists is important. If the cameraman remembers the principles of composition, he should have no difficulty in offering well-composed, interesting shots. He should constantly bear in mind the suggestions regarding triangulation and intersection of thirds, and he must avoid symmetrical layouts at all costs.

It is often impossible to present interesting shots on such pro-grammes as panel games and quiz shows, where it is common to have two or three people sitting in line behind a desk. The group shot can sometimes be taken from a little to one side, thereby introducing some diagonal lines into the picture. But this is not always possible, and the cameraman must resign himself to the fact that he can add nothing visually to the programme.

Shots of people who are sitting behind desks can often be very irritating to take. If the eyes are placed in the correct position in the frame, the desk might bisect the picture. If the desk is correctly placed, the headroom will probably be wrong and the composition will be unbalanced. In this case the cameraman should settle for the best framing so far as the artists are concerned. They are the main points of interest in the shot, and such things as desks must be left to take care of themselves.

But when artists can be manoeuvred into various positions, they must be grouped in such a way that the eye is led unfailingly towards the person or persons designated as the centre of interest. And remember, high camera positions tend to add significance to background subjects, and low positions emphasize foreground subjects.

Looking Room

When an artist looks towards one side of the shot—whether he is seen in profile, semi-profile, or with his head turned just a little from the square-on position—the cameraman must leave a certain amount of space between the artist's eyes and the edge of frame into which the artist can look. This space is known as "looking room", and the cameraman must be very careful to leave the correct amount if he is to compose his shot in a balanced and attractive manner.

What is the correct amount of looking room that should be allowed? The answer is that it all depends on just how far the artist has turned his head towards the side of frame. More looking room must be allowed for a full-profile shot than for a semi-profile shot.

Fortunately there is a little tip which will help the trainee cameraman to achieve some standardization in the amount of looking room he should allow on various shots. Obviously, as soon as the artist turns his head to one side, one eye will be nearer the camera than the other. Imagine a vertical line running from the top of frame to the bottom, which exactly bisects the picture. If the artist is framed so that this imaginary line runs through the junction of the artist's nose and *near* eye, the space between the artist's face and the edge of frame will represent the correct amount of looking room.

This suggestion holds good for all variations of profile shots, and helps prevent the basic mistake of allowing too much looking room.

Cameramen must not forget that they must also allow looking

108

Fig. 39. *Left:* The artist has been framed in the centre of the shot. This is wrong. *Right:* This is correct. Looking-room has been allowed in front of him.

room when the artist is facing towards the top or bottom of frame. The subject must be given space in front of his eyes—and it must not be too much or too little. It is all too easy for the cameraman to unbalance a shot if he is careless over applying this principle of correct looking room.

There are, however, two occasions when looking room is increased beyond these recommended amounts: (i) when the artist is looking at something which is actually included in the shot and (ii) when some object or highlight occupies the looking room, which is then increased slightly in the interests of good composition.

And there is one occasion when the cameraman deliberately leaves *no* looking room. This is when it is desired to convey a sense of isolation or loneliness to an artist who is looking towards the side of frame. This feeling can be heightened if the cameraman

Fig. 40. *Left:* No looking-room has been allowed—this is a badly composed shot. *Right:* The centre line of the frame runs through the junction of the artist's nose and near eye. This ensures that the correct amount of looking-room is provided.

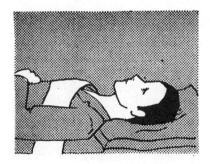

Fig. 41. Cameramen sometimes forget that they must allow looking-room when an artist faces the top of frame. The same rules apply, of course, when the artist is looking towards the bottom of frame.

Fig. 42. The looking-room has been increased to include the object of the artist's attention. In fact this framing would be the automatic outcome of any attempts at conscientious composition.

Fig. 43. The artist is looking towards the top left-hand corner and the correct amount of looking-room has been allowed. This is a well-composed shot.

This is even better. The highlight balances the shot and the looking-room has been calculated in relation to this highlight.

Fig. 44. If the director cuts between these two shots we shall know that the artists are, in fact, facing each other.

frames the shot in such a way that there is very little space between the artist and the edge of frame.

While on this question of looking room, there is an interesting point which arises from it. When two artists are apparently holding a telephone conversation with each other, the normal practice is to cover this with two cameras, one for each artist. The director can then cut between the two shots as each artist speaks or reacts to what is being said.

Although it might not be important that these two shots should match each other in size, it is essential that the two artists should not be framed so that they are both facing the same way. If artist A is looking towards the right-hand side of the shot, then artist B must look towards the left-hand side.

This does not happen in real life, of course, but it must be

Fig. 45. Intercutting between these two shots, however, suggests that the artists have their backs to each other. This sensation has been achieved by deliberately placing the artists' heads near the edge of frame.

111

arranged in this manner on a television programme. If it is ignored there will be something vaguely wrong with the sequence—the artists will not appear to be talking to each other.

General Rules

Before going on to specific problems of framing, there are a few points worth mentioning.

Artists must never be framed in such a way that articles or pieces of scenery appear to grow out of their heads. If these offending objects cannot be moved, the cameraman must move his camera a little to one side—or vary its height—in order to cancel out this effect.

Avoid a dead frontal approach whenever possible. A slight change of camera angle can invariably add interest to a shot.

The advice that symmetry should be avoided is repeated. But shots must be balanced in accordance with the principles of composition.

Avoid framing shots in such a way that horizontal lines in the scene appear to rest on the artist's head. And horizontal and vertical lines should never bisect the picture—the ideal place for them is about one-third of the distance in from the edges of frame.

Cameramen sometimes forget that the line formed by the junction of the studio floor with the background set can bisect the picture, despite the fact that the shot is otherwise well composed. This fault often occurs when the cameraman is shooting a dance item. The subject is so all-absorbing that in his efforts to follow the movements of the dancer in a competent, artistic manner, the

Fig. 46. *Left:* The cameraman has framed the dancer correctly—with twice as much headroom as footroom—but he has ignored the fact that the horizontal line in the background bisects the shot. *Right:* Lowering the camera has moved this horizontal line on to the lower third of the picture. It is no longer distracting, and our attention is rivetted on the dancer.

cameraman might not notice that his picture is bisected by a horizontal line.

This will probably never happen if he shoots these items from a low or a high position. In fact, low-angle shots of dancers are probably the most attractive. Never be satisfied because the centre of interest is correctly framed—always check that other features of the scene are not distracting elements.

And always remember that the correct height of the camera for each shot is as important as the choice of lens and camera angle, the rules of composition, and all the other points which must be borne in mind when lining up a shot.

8

FRAMING MUSICIANS

THE trainee cameraman might appreciate some advice on the framing of certain, specialized shots that commonly occur in television programmes. Among the most common of these are shots of musical instruments.

It can safely be said that there is no new way to shoot a pianist at a piano. The repertoire of shots has been exhausted, and it is a waste of time and effort to try and discover novel ways of presenting this subject. The same can be said of other musical instruments, and it is far better to concentrate on shooting these subjects in such a way that the viewer can enjoy the technique and artistry of the player.

The Pianist

The *basic* shot of a pianist, then, should obviously include his hands, and some detail of his face. A medium long shot or long shot taken at an angle of no more than 45 degrees to the piano keyboard is the safest basic approach. On no account should the pianist be placed in the centre of the shot. He should be towards the edge of frame, with the piano stretched out before him.

For close shots showing detail of the fingering, the camera should look almost along the line of the keyboard to prevent the artist's arms and body obscuring the shot. These shots are usually taken with narrow-angle lenses—small depth of field remember—and the cameraman must concentrate hard if he is to keep the hands in his shot, and hold focus. His main difficulty will occur when the hands spread, leaving him with the problem of deciding which hand to follow and hold focus on.

In this case the hand nearer the camera must be singled out. And since the artist's right hand will normally carry the main melody of any composition, the camera should always shoot from the artist's right—except when a special effect is called for.

114

Fig. 47. Typical M.S. (*left*) and M.L.S. (*right*) of pianist. Note angle of keyboard and position of artist.

Close shots of the keyboard are best taken from a high camera position. Since these will be required for short periods only, or for selected passages, these close shots can be most effective if the cameraman memorizes the actual hand movements during them. Then he will never be caught unprepared for a sudden musical run or fast passage. The hands of the virtuoso pianist can move with bewildering speed, and if the cameraman is unprepared, the full effect of his shot might well be lost.

Most directors will want a shot of the artist's face at some time during a musical item. These shots are often quite interesting since the facial expressions of an artist at work are worth recording. The best position for the camera is in the well of the piano, from where useful close-ups of the pianist can be taken. If the lid of the piano can be opened, the artist can be attractively framed in the triangle formed by the top of the piano, the lid, and the stay which holds the lid in its open position.

If this shot is taken with a normal or wide-angle lens, it is often possible to crab the camera around the side of the piano until it is once more shooting the artist and keyboard.

Fig. 48. An attractive method of using the lid and prop of the piano as a triangular frame around the artist.

The subject of camera movement will be dealt with in a later chapter. But it will do no harm to remind the cameraman here that any camera movement during a musical item must be in sympathy with the mood of the music. Slow passages of music call for slow, almost imperceptible camera moves, while fast, exciting moves should be attempted only during fast passages of music.

Shooting the pianist's feet is never satisfactory. There is little to interest the viewer after a few seconds, and the shot will invariably be of poor quality due to the lack of light.

The cameraman can sometimes offer dramatic shots by moving his camera close to the keyboard—and below the level of it—and then tilting up to include the artist's face as well as his hands. This can be held for a few seconds to provide a startling effect, but he must ensure that he is not entering another cameraman's shot or casting unwanted shadows.

When tracking out from a close-up of the pianist's hands to a long shot, the cameraman must never allow these hands to vanish out of the bottom of frame, and then reappear. Not only will he deprive the viewer of the main point of interest, but the movement will have become obtrusive—and that must never be allowed to happen.

Very long shots of a piano depend very much for their success on the settings used in the scene. If the floor has been dramatically lit to provide interesting shadows or lighting effects, or if the floor has been carefully treated, the piano should be framed in the top half of the shot. If, however, the background consists of well-arranged drapes or lighting effects, then the best position for the piano will be towards the lower half of the shot.

Fig. 49. *Left:* In this V.L.S. use has been made of the decorated floor in order to frame the artist in the upper third of the shot. *Right:* The artist has been attractively framed in the lower third of the shot with the use of background dressings.

The cameraman must remember to perform all his movements as quietly as possible during soft passages of music, particularly when he is engaged in shooting a classical music item. Any noise would be likely to distract the viewer, and (what is even worse) the artist. The amount of concentration required from a concert pianist is very high. *The cameraman would be committing an artistic sin were he to do anything which might disturb an artist.*

The Violinist

Shots of violinists can be a real headache for the trainee cameraman. In most cases the director will require close shots of the artist and his instrument, and the cameraman might have to resort to the use of narrow-angle lenses. Since many violinists are apt to indulge in incredibly violent movements during their performances, the cameraman might have some difficulty in keeping the artist in shot. Focusing, too, can be quite a nightmare, and the cameraman can do nothing but concentrate and hope for the best.

Once again the best angle for the camera is about 45 degrees to the instrument, though the position of the violin will change rapidly during the item. Despite many directors' views to the contrary, there is little to interest the viewer in a close shot of the bow passing over the strings—certainly for not more than a few seconds. Any big close-ups, then, should be directed at the violinist's fingers or face.

Trying to shoot a close-up which includes both these features will never be wholly successful. There is often so little depth of field available that one or the other must be out of focus. In these circumstances it is far better to concentrate focus on the fingers—which will be in foreground—than to settle for a close-up of the face which will be marred by the out-of-focus violin and hand continually obscuring the shot.

If the piece of music is particularly long it is worth attempting to vary the shots a little. The viewer can become bored by the presentation of only two or three different shots on a solitary artist.

But this search for varying shots should not be carried to the ridiculous. No shot should be offered which would distract the viewer's attention from the quality of the artist's performance.

It is more desirable, artistically, to vary the shots by introducing camera movement, than to resort to "gimmick" shots to relieve the apparent monotony.

Some interesting shots can be obtained, however, by shooting the artist from a low camera position, particularly if the camera

Fig. 50. A high shot from behind the violinist's right shoulder is an interesting variation from the more standard types of shots.

moves close to the artist. A high shot taken from behind the artist's right arm—the bowing arm—will provide an excellent view of the violinist's fingers and head movements.

Very long shots, once again, depend for their success on the dressings provided. A violinist normally occupies a comparatively small part of a very long shot, and the picture must be augmented with some form of dressing if the shot is to be interesting.

Placing the violinist on a rostrum will provide a useful base to the shot, and discreet lighting effects (or carefully arranged drapes) can complete the picture. Opening the item with the artist silhouetted against a light background is very popular, and it is certainly effective. The lighting director can do much to ensure the success of these very long shots, particularly in the use of shadows, lighting effects, and carefully rehearsed lighting changes.

The violin is a quieter instrument than the piano, and once again the cameraman is reminded to keep unavoidable noise to a minimum.

Fig. 51. *Left:* The set dressings have been used to provide an artificial top of frame, and the artist has been nicely framed in relation to them. *Right:* Where a boom microphone must be used, the artist must be near the top of frame. Here, the steps have been used to achieve this and maintain a balanced shot.

Other Instrumentalists

Guitars offer a little more scope to the cameraman than violins. The hands plucking the strings provide an additional source of shots, and since the instrument is larger than a violin, the problem of restricted depth of field is somewhat lessened. Apart from this the technique is similar for both instruments, though it will be found that most guitarists move very little during their performance. This makes the cameraman's task a little easier.

Shots of 'cellos and double-basses usually fall into one of the following categories—since they are rarely used as solo instruments: (i) L.S. artist and instrument, (ii) M.S. including fingering hand, (iii) C.U. bowing or plucking hand, and (iv) tilting the camera from shot (ii) to (iii), or vice versa.

They present no special problems, and should be well within the capabilities of any cameraman.

Shots of wind instruments present no extra problems, though there still remains the difficulty of holding focus on very close shots. Although close-ups of the player's fingers are often quite interesting, the effect will be more pleasing if the player's face is included.

The treatment of solo harp items is similar to that for pianos. Once again the safest angle is no more than the 45-degree line, and the camera should approach the harp from the side controlled by the artist's left hand. Harps are invariably rested on the artist's right shoulder, and approaching from the artist's left ensures unrestricted close-ups of the face.

Occasional shots from the right-hand side of the harp provide interesting close-ups of the artist's face seen through the strings. But the shots preceding or following them should not include the artist's face if the camera is shooting the left-hand side of the harp. This leads to the disturbing effect of the artist appearing to look to different sides of frame as the shots are taken.

All that has been said about very long shots on other solo instruments applies here. The harp has one advantage so far as the cameraman is concerned. The ornamental decorations, which are a common feature of this instrument, present a very useful focusing check.

Drummers, surrounded as they are by a variety of drums and cymbals, are difficult subjects to shoot neatly. The best shots are those taken from a high camera position. Since it is normal to mount drummers on high rostra, however, this is not always possible. The best plan is to forget about any attempts to cover the artist's movements from an instructive point of view, and concentrate on getting the maximum dramatic value out of the shot.

Placing the camera as low as possible and moving close to the subject will provide an interesting angle, as will shots taken from just behind one of the drummer's arms. Big close-ups of whirling sticks and trembling cymbals can hold their interest for a few seconds only.

9

EARLY TECHNIQUES

WHEN shooting two-shots in which the two artists are not the same distance from the camera, the cameraman is sometimes faced with the problem of deciding which artist should be sharply focused. This situation arises if we are taking a two-shot favouring the far artist, with most of the features of the near artist visible in the shot.

Splitting Focus

The normal solution is to use the available depth of field. It is often found that if the camera is focused on a point somewhere between the two subjects, they will both fall within the depth of field and be acceptably in focus. This is known as splitting focus.

But where splitting focus will not solve the problem, the cameraman should either request that the artists are placed closer together, or focus on the far artist—whom he is favouring. But the far artist should not be focused sharply to the exclusion of the near artist. The cameraman should move the point of sharpest focus from the split focus position towards the far artist, until he is *acceptably* sharp. The near artist will not then be as "soft" as he would have been had the cameraman concentrated focus entirely on the far artist.

This is fairly straightforward. The greatest confusion seems to arise when two artists are facing the camera, one very close to it and the other much farther away. This sort of shot is very common in television plays. If the near artist were doing all the talking there would be no problem—the cameraman would focus on him.

But if they are holding a conversation, what is the cameraman to do? Should he focus on the near artist; or the far one; or should he focus on each one in turn as they speak—in other words throw focus from one to the other.

Throwing Focus

This last method of throwing focus, although it is occasionally seen, cannot be recommended. It is distracting to the viewer, and makes him conscious of camerawork. And if the conversation passes back and forth very quickly, the technique becomes a little ridiculous and finally irritating. It is all too easy, too, for the cameraman to lag a little behind these changes of emphasis, and ruin the effect.

This technique cannot be justified, then, although it provides the cameraman with an interesting exercise in the application of his skill.

There can be only one answer to this problem. *If the near artist is facing the camera, and very close to it, he must be the object of focus.* It does not matter that the far artist is holding a conversation with him. The very fact that the near artist has been placed in such a prominent position in the shot—and occupying the major part of it, almost certainly—indicates that his facial expressions are important. The cameraman must focus on him, then, to the exclusion of everything else.

If the director wants the emphasis to switch from one artist to the other, then the near artist must be made to face the far one as this change of significance takes place. The cameraman must then move focus on to the far artist *as* the near artist turns his head. This change of focus must be timed to start the instant the near artist moves his head, and finish as the turn is completed. Performed this way the change of focus will be accomplished quite unobtrusively.

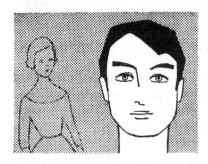

Fig. 52. *Left:* Although both artists are facing the camera, and speaking, the cameraman must focus on the near artist. *Right:* If the director wishes to make the far artist the centre of interest, the near artist must be made to face her. The cameraman must then focus on this new centre of interest.

Immediately the near artist faces the camera again, the cameraman must refocus on him—once again *during* the turn of the head.

This technique of switching focus from one subject to another is sometimes called "plopping" or throwing focus. It is something that every cameraman will be called upon to perform sooner or later, and he should occupy some of his free time in the studio in practising it.

He should practise "plopping" focus at different speeds, over varying distances, and on all lenses. There is quite a variation in the amount of adjustment needed under different conditions. The cameraman must be adept at this technique before he is required to put it into practice during transmission of a programme.

Defocus Mixes

Directors are very fond of using a technique known as a defocus mix in order to provide a transition from one scene to another.

Here, the picture which is being transmitted is slowly defocused, the director mixes (or dissolves) to a second defocused picture of another scene, and when the transition from one defocused picture to the other has been completed, the second picture is slowly brought into focus.

Since the cameraman is responsible for the mechanics of this operation he must consider the following problems: (i) should he defocus his picture by focusing progressively forward towards the camera until his picture is completely soft? (ii) should he accomplish this by focusing back away from the camera? (iii) if he is the second camera in the transition, should he refocus by focusing back or forward? and (iv) does it matter anyway?

To answer the last question first, it does matter—very much. The others can be answered by stating that he must always *defocus* his picture by focusing *forward*, and *refocus* by focusing *back*.

A moment's thought will reveal why this is so. If the cameraman attempts to defocus his picture by focusing back, he will only succeed in transferring focus from the main subject to the background. His picture will probably never be soft enough to make the transition a success. Focusing forward, however, will invariably throw everything in the scene, including foreground objects, completely out of focus.

Similarly, if he is the second camera in the transition, he cannot refocus by focusing forward. There are two reasons for this. In the first place, since the first picture was defocused by focusing forward, the viewer will subconsciously expect the refocusing to be a reversal of that movement—in other words by focusing back.

Secondly, if he focuses forward in order to refocus his picture, the background will become sharp before the main subject—who will be an out-of-focus blur in the foreground. Obviously this is undesirable.

The speed at which the cameraman should defocus and refocus will usually be between two and three seconds in practice.

Captions

The shooting of captions, maps, diagrams, photographs, and similar subjects does not receive the attention from many cameramen that it deserves.

Perhaps the show is coming to an end, and the cameraman has taken all his live shots in the programme. All that remains are two captions—one for the designer's credit and one for the director's—then he can go home. It is all too common in these circumstances to point the camera in the general direction of the caption board, adjust the shot until the letters look reasonably parallel to the bottom of frame, and lock the panning head.

But this is just not good enough. If something is worth taking a shot of, it deserves some attention. It is not uncommon at the end of many television programmes to be disturbed by end-captions which lean in different directions; or vary in size; or appear in different parts of the frame.

These untidy shots are usually the result of sloppy, indifferent camerawork. And the blame must lie with the cameraman, for he is spoiling the ship for a ha'p'orth of tar.

The pity of it all is that it is so unnecessary. There is nothing simpler than shooting captions correctly—and therein probably lies the root of the trouble. They are so simple to shoot that the cameraman is tempted to leave them to look after themselves. And the sad fact is that they just will not look after themselves.

There are three basic points which the cameraman must consider when he is shooting captions: (i) the lens he should use, (ii) the height of his camera, and (iii) the position of his camera in relation to the caption. We can look at each of these a little closer.

Which Lens ?

Obviously much depends on the size of the caption; how much of it the cameraman is expected to frame; whether any camera movement is required; how close the camera is expected to be to

124

the caption. There are many things to be considered before the most suitable lens can be decided upon.

If the cameraman uses a wide-angle lens to shoot a standard sized caption, he will probably have to place his camera so close to the caption that it might well be in the shadow thrown by the camera. On the other hand, he should not use a very narrow angle lens. He would be forced to place camera and caption so far apart that there is the danger of people walking between them when the shot is being transmitted. Furthermore, this lens makes precise line-up of the caption more difficult (as handling is coarser), and even slight vibration of the camera head shows as considerable judder on the screen.

Since the majority of captions used in television studios are of a standard size the most suitable lens for shooting them is the intermediate lens (14 to 17 degrees). The use of this lens ensures that the distance from the camera to the caption will not be too great or too small. And if a supplementary light is mounted on the camera—as in many studios—this lens will usually place the camera at the correct distance to take advantage of the light.

Captions are normally mounted on specially designed easels. The best of these have a frame into which the captions are slotted. Ideally this frame should be spring-loaded as this ensures that the captions are held rigidly in place. There is the further advantage that if the top caption is pulled out, the next will be pushed forward to take its place. This eliminates any need for the cameraman to refocus on each new caption.

Sometimes the cameraman is required to frame very small captions or photographs. This situation is common on news bulletins when the only available photograph of someone who is suddenly in the news might be a family snapshot. Contrary to what might appear to be common sense, a narrow-angle lens is not the lens which should be used for this type of shot—and this applies whenever very small subjects are placed in front of the camera.

The reason for this is quite straightforward. A narrow-angle lens has a large minimum focusing distance—i.e. it cannot be focused on objects very close to the camera. If this lens is used in an attempt to frame very small subjects, then, the cameraman might easily find that he will be unable to focus the lens on them if they are moved close enough to his camera to fill the frame.

Since normal and wide-angle lenses allow the camera to be moved quite close to subjects, therefore, they should always be used when small captions or other tiny subjects have to be framed. And special lighting will have to be directed at these subjects to eliminate the camera shadow which will invariably fall on them.

Large captions, such as maps, require the use of normal or wide-angle lenses, since the camera would almost certainly be an impractical distance away with an intermediate lens.

If the director wants the camera to move towards or away from a caption, the cameraman must make every effort to use a normal or wide-angle lens—even if it means special lighting.

A lens with an angle of view of 20 degrees and over should be the automatic choice for this situation, and the intermediate lens should be used only if it is impossible to accommodate a wider angle lens. On no account should narrow-angle lenses be used. These rule out any possibility of smooth camera movement, and increase the focusing problems.

Intermediate lenses for captions, then. But normal or wide-angle lenses if the captions are very small, or very big, or if camera movement is required during the shot.

What Camera Height ?

The most neglected aspect of caption shooting is the attention paid to the height of the camera. The camera must always be at right-angles to the plane of the caption—it is as simple as that. If the camera lens axis is not at right angles to the surface we shall be conscious of the effect known as "keystoning". If the camera looks up at the caption, vertical lines will appear to converge as they rise in the frame, and they will appear to diverge if the camera looks down at the caption.

The cameraman has only to look out of his viewfinder for a second, to check that his camera is horizontal, for this fault never to arise. The closer the camera is taken to a caption, the more noticeable will be the keystone distortion of incorrect camera position.

On occasions, the cameraman is required to frame a caption in such a way that some of the letters appear at the bottom of his shot. If these letters are in the centre of the caption, the tendency is to adjust the height of the camera until it is shooting at right-angles to the centre of the caption. The cameraman then tilts up until the letters are placed at the bottom of his shot. This is bad practice. The camera must be raised until it is shooting at right-angles to the actual letters when they are in the correct position in the shot.

126

camera so that it is correct for the end of the movement, i.e. when the camera is closest to the caption.

The reason is obvious. Keystoning is more noticeable the closer the camera is to a caption, and it is better to settle for a slightly incorrect height at the far position of the camera: keystone distortion will not be so noticeable there.

What Camera Position ?

The camera must always be placed so that it is square-on to a caption. As we saw in an earlier chapter, immediately the camera is moved so that it is shooting a subject at an angle, diagonal lines appear in the shot. This is all very well for most shots; but it is fatal so far as captions are concerned.

Unless the camera is square-on to a caption, the letters will not appear to be horizontal. If the camera shoots from the left, the letters will rise towards the right-hand side of frame. In extreme cases they will get noticeably smaller as they rise.

It is very important, then, that the camera should always be square-on to a caption. And this is particularly so when the cameraman is asked to track towards or away from a caption. An example will illustrate this point.

Let us assume that the cameraman has framed a shot of a rather large map of the world, and he is then asked to track into a country which is on the left-hand side of this map. He must place his camera at right-angles to the map for the long shot—that is obvious. But he should not track in along this centre line. If he does, he will end up by shooting the close-up of the single country from an acute angle.

He should place the camera close to the single country and square-on to it and mark on the floor the position of the camera; then reposition the camera to the long shot, square-on position and mark the floor accordingly. The direction of the track will now be along a line drawn between these two camera positions. It will be at an angle to the map; in this case a diagonal track to the left.

He will be square-on for the long shot, square-on for the close-up, and the line of his track will take him inevitably to the country he is singling out. Pivoting—which we shall explain in a later chapter—will almost be done for him, and he can concentrate on focusing. This is the method he must always adopt when tracking, particularly when it is directed at captions.

Finally, once a caption has been framed correctly, and provided no camera movement is required, the panning head should be locked. It is very unwise to attempt to hold a shot of a caption absolutely still without the mechanical aid of the pan and tilt locks on the panning head. The slightest movement of the camera will be reflected on the shot, and moving captions are quite disturbing to look at—particularly when they are meant to be static!

When the cameraman is shooting subjects other than captions, he must attempt to keep the camera still without locking the panning head. This can be achieved only if the cameraman is relaxed. Gripping the camera and the panning handle, digging his heels into the floor, and gritting his teeth will merely provide ideal conditions for the transmission of any body movement to the shot. In extreme cases the shot will move in time with the cameraman's breathing.

It is possible, with experience, to acquire a grip on the camera which is firm yet light. That might sound paradoxical, but it is a fact nevertheless. And the basis of this technique is relaxation. In fact the cameraman must be relaxed in his mind as well as in his body. Any tenseness will be reflected, not only in the quality of his shots, but also in the manner in which he carries out the actual technique of camerawork in all its forms.

The experienced cameraman, in common with experts in other fields, makes the job look easy. He is alert, yet relaxed. He does not seem to hurry unduly, yet his moves are fast and safe. There is a general air of quiet confidence about him which singles him out among others not so experienced. But above all, he is relaxed.

10

PANNING AND TILTING

CAMERA movement can be divided into the following forms:

1. Panning—horizontal pivoting of the camera head.
2. Tilting—vertical pivoting of the camera head.
3. Tracking—movement of the camera towards or away from a subject. (Also known as dollying in or out.)
4. Crabbing—movement of the camera across a scene and parallel to it.

These are the four basic and most commonly used movements. More often than not, three—sometimes all four—have to be performed simultaneously. Unless these manoeuvres are handled correctly, any television production—and the cameraman's reputation!—will suffer.

The camera can also be elevated and depressed by raising and lowering the central column of the dolly. The success of this operation depends mainly on the type of dolly in use. Some designs lend themselves to this movement; others are not suitable.

"Craning up", "craning down", and "tonguing" (or gibbing), are movements that are performed with a camera mounted on a manually-tracked or motorized dolly.

In this chapter, we deal only with panning and tilting. Crabbing and tracking form the subject of the next chapter and the other movements are discussed in Chapter 12.

The golden rule for all camera movement is that it must be unobtrusive. The responsibility for ensuring this lies jointly with the director and the cameraman.

The Director's Responsibility

There should always be a reason for any camera movement. Instructing the cameraman to track or crab merely in order to break the monotony, has the unfortunate effect of appearing just that on the screen. The camera should track in because the director wants to take the viewer closer to a subject, because he has something to show him. If the production of a programme is well handled, this will coincide with the viewer's desire to be taken closer. The camera should pan only when the viewer is expected, or required, to shift his attention from say, one person to another.

Movement is more easily kept unobtrusive if it is motivated by action within the frame. If, for instance, an actor looks to his right with a gasp of amazement, the viewer almost begs to be shown what has caught the actor's attention. On the rare occasions when the director does not wish to cut to another camera, a pan is an alternative.

In the above example there is no doubt that cutting from one camera to another is more natural than panning. But if the camera is panned *as* the artist turns his head, the movement will be motivated. There will be a reason for the pan followed by a definite inducement to initiate the movement. The viewer will not be conscious of the actual pan: he will notice only the effect it produces.

Moving the camera to coincide with the actions of artists has another advantage: flaws in technique, such as camera shake or irregularities in a track, will be less noticeable. The viewer's attention will be concentrated on the action taking place, and the mechanics of the camera movement will not distract him. If the camera movement can be timed to start when the artist starts to move, and to finish when he stops moving, then the movement of the camera is likely to be a success, both artistically and technically.

But of course it is often necessary to move the camera in relation to a static scene. In this situation the success of the movement will depend entirely on the skill of the cameraman. And this leads us on to the study of the cameraman's responsibilities, and his techniques.

At this stage it may be worth pointing out that although it is the director's responsibility to provide reasons and motivations for camera movement, this does not mean that the cameraman should detach himself from these considerations. If he does, his work will not be in sympathy with the director's intentions, and his technique will remain artistically inferior.

The Cameraman's Responsibility

It is the cameraman's duty to ensure that all movements of his camera are performed smoothly. Bad technique in camera move-

130

ment, more than any other feature of camerawork, can destroy the viewer's concentration. And that is a sin the cameraman must never be guilty of.

How many times have we seen a picture that shudders and sways as the camera tracks, apparently over a bed of stones? At the end of the track the final shot is framed—clearly with relief—two or three seconds after the camera dolly has stopped moving. And then a hurried correction of focus follows . . . just as an after-thought.

This is bad camerawork—not only because the technique offends the purists, but also because the viewer has almost certainly been made aware of this badly executed camera movement, and as a result his concentration has been disturbed.

How can we avoid uneven, distracting movement?

In the first place, to be entirely practical, the panning head on the dolly must be correctly adjusted (see page 45). It must be evenly balanced, and the pan and tilt adjustment screws carefully set. If the screws are too loose, the camera will sway with the slightest movement. In this situation, holding a static shot is difficult; controlled movement impossible. On the other hand, if the screws are too tight, the cameraman will find that he is having to strain to move the camera, and compensating movements will emerge as a series of sudden, short jerks.

Remember, too, that the screws should be so adjusted that the pressure on the tilt friction equals that on the pan friction. Unless this is done, combined panning and tilting cannot be performed smoothly.

Correct friction setting is a matter for the individual. There is no hard and fast rule: it depends on the cameraman's strength and muscular control. But it is important that the cameraman should give some thought to finding the friction settings that suit him personally. All too often this very important consideration is overlooked.

No cameraman should ever be caught unprepared for a track or crab, with the wheels of the dolly pointing away from the line of the proposed movement. And yet many a cameraman has found himself in this predicament—usually after a hurried dash from another part of the studio. The planned camera movement is invariably delayed while the cameraman re-aligns his dolly, and attempts at the same time to keep the camera steady—usually without success. Most cameramen have fallen into this trap, but no good cameraman allows it to happen to him twice.

Always start and finish a pan with a static shot. The pan itself should be smooth; it should have a constant speed throughout (except when following uneven movement); and it should end at the same speed at which it started.

This practice of beginning and ending a pan with a static shot applies to other forms of camera movement too. Occasionally a cut will be made from one moving camera to another moving camera. But normally this is done only for effect. For all normal purposes no camera movement is complete unless it is a smooth transition from one steady shot to another.

There are occasions when the cameraman must ask himself whether or not he should pan at all. We know that obtrusive camera movement is disturbing, and yet the action on the screen might seem to call for a series of short pans.

The Animated Artist ·

This situation often arises when the cameraman frames a medium close-up of a voluble, animated artist. Some people move their heads and bodies a great deal when they are talking earnestly, and seem to do their best to throw themselves out of the cameraman's M.C.U.

The inexperienced cameraman's natural reaction is to follow each of these sudden movements in an attempt to keep the artist correctly framed at all times. But this can be terribly distracting, and more often than not the cameraman will find that he is always a little behind the artist's movements.

Whenever possible the cameraman must resist the temptation to pan with each little movement the artist makes. He should allow the artist to move around within the frame, even if these movements take him near the edges of the shot. This technique is quite acceptable provided there is no danger of the artist actually moving his head out of the frame. And once the artist has completed his burst of movement he will invariably settle into his original position.

Of course, if the movements are so violent that the cameraman cannot hold the artist in a static shot, then he must pan. But he should delay these pans until the artist is very near the edge of the shot, and then pan only as much as is necessary to keep the artist framed. And these pans must be smooth—not sudden and jerky—if the movement is to be kept unobtrusive.

132

In fairness to the cameraman, the director should not expect him to hold an animated artist in a shot as tight as a medium close-up. A mid-shot is more appropriate under these circumstances.

Subject to Subject

When the cameraman is expected to pan from one subject to another, it is extremely bad technique to pan past the new subject, and then reverse the movement to get the desired shot. This need never happen if the movement has been properly practised by the cameraman—repeated over and over again until the movement is flawless. After all, this is what rehearsals are for.

When panning from one person to another, beware of variations in height between them. If two or more persons of exactly equal height do exist, they never seem to find the opportunity to talk to each other in front of a television camera! Panning from one artist to another, therefore, usually involves tilting the camera too. But the pan and tilt must be combined to produce a steady, diagonal progression from one shot to another. This, like everything else, needs practice, then more practice, until it is perfect.

Remember, too, that when panning from one subject to another, refocusing may be necessary if they are not equidistant from the camera. Even the smoothest pan can be marred by the cameraman focusing too early—or too late—on his new subject. The secret is to imagine the pan through the eyes of the viewer, refocusing as his interest is transferred from the first subject to the second. Quite large changes of focus can be made, undetected, if this tip is remembered.

A possible motivation for a pan occurs when an artist turns his head to face a new subject—the object of the pan. In this case the

Fig. 53. *Left:* The cameraman must never pan horizontally then tilt down to the boy. *Right:* Panning from a high to a lower subject should be in the form of a diagonal progression.

133

pan should start *with* the turn of the head (not before it, or after it) and the movement will be finished before the viewer realizes what has happened.

The Long Fast Pan

Smooth panning is most difficult to accomplish when the camera has to be panned through an angle of 90 degrees or more. In the case of a slow pan the cameraman can, with practice, move quite smoothly around the dolly, keeping his viewfinder in sight throughout.

But there are occasions when the speed of the pan will not allow the cameraman time to move his body or feet. He must then stand so that he is comfortably placed for the *end* of the pan. Placing the body for the beginning of the pan is bad technique, for it can lead to a gradually worsening pan, a badly framed final shot and, in some cases, an overbalanced cameraman!

Experience has proved the first method to be the better. The cameraman usually has a few seconds at least in which to prepare for his manoeuvre. He should carefully frame the first shot, and having done so, he should move his body into position for the end of the pan—taking care not to disturb the camera as he does so. Even though the viewfinder may not be visible from this new position, the cameraman knows that he is offering a correctly framed shot. As the pan progresses his control over the camera will improve, and the final framing will then be a simple matter.

When panning with a moving artist, the speed of the pan is naturally governed by the speed of the moving subject. He should be held roughly in centre frame throughout—with slightly more space in front of him than behind him—and the pan should stop when he stops. If the artist is moving across the scene to join another person, the pan should be speeded up towards the end of the movement to include the extra subject. If this is done correctly, a well-composed two-shot will be framed as soon as the two artists come together.

Static Scenes

It is sometimes necessary to pan across a static scene, or across a photograph or painting mounted as a caption. In such cases, it is often not important to the production whether the pan is made from left to right, or from right to left. When there is a choice, a pan from left to right usually seems to be the more pleasing.

134

This may well be because in the Western world we read from left to right, and our eyes are therefore more accustomed to travelling in that direction when taking in detail. This is not to say that we always look from left to right when surveying a scene. But if we pan in that direction on the screen, the viewer is more likely to subconsciously accept the movement as being completely natural.

Panning Across the Set

Sometimes an artist will enter a scene through a doorway, or perform a similar action which brings him into an otherwise empty shot. He may then have to be panned to another part of the set.

This is one of the many eventualities for which the cameraman must prepare himself. He should stand so that he is comfortably placed for the end of the pan. During rehearsals he will line up the shot in such a way that the artist is correctly framed as he appears. To accomplish this, the artist first stands in the doorway, and the cameraman composes his opening shot—paying particular attention to headroom. The cameraman mentally notes where the top and sides of his frame are cutting the set, so that subsequently he will always secure this same framing again when composing this particular shot.

It may be that the top of the frame runs through a distinctive mark on the set; or across the top of the door frame; or through a particular pattern on the wallpaper. There is usually some such identification of the framing that can easily be remembered. This is the only way to be sure of offering the director exactly the same shot on every rehearsal.

When panning an artist across a set to exit through a door, the cameraman must be sure not to pan *farther* than the door. In this situation he should note, on rehearsals, where the edges of his frame are cutting the set—and stop panning as soon as he has reached those marks.

Ballet Dancers

Panning with dancers, particularly ballet dancers, requires a certain technique of its own if the effect is to be pleasing and the camera movement unobtrusive.

Probably due to the self-discipline necessary in their profession, ballet dancers are usually the most reliable of artists. If asked to

135

end a certain movement on a particular spot, they will usually oblige time after time. And this makes the cameraman's job a little easier.

When covering a ballet item, the cameraman must pay careful attention to the speed and "flow" of his pans, to be sure that they are in sympathy with the mood of the performance. The technique of allying camera movement with mood is something that all good cameramen possess.

It is *not* good technique to keep the dancers in centre of frame, panning with them every time they move to right or left. Dancers change direction constantly, and sometimes suddenly, and to attempt to hold their every move in the middle of the frame represents very untidy camerawork.

As an example, assume that the dancers are performing in the centre of frame and that they are soon to move left. The distance they will travel is such that they will move out of shot unless the cameraman pans left. And they will not stay in this new position for longer than a few seconds.

The shot should be held static until the dancers have moved into the left-hand third of the frame. When they have reached this point, the cameraman should "flow" into his pan. He should then continue the pan at the same speed as the dancers' movements, keeping them at the same distance from the left-hand edge of his frame as they were when he started the camera movement.

As the dancers move to the right again, the cameraman must vary the speed of his pan in a most subtle manner. At first he must pan slower than the dancers to allow them to move into the centre of his frame. Once there, the pan must be speeded up to coincide with the speed of the dancers.

Once the middle of the set occupies the centre of the frame again, the cameraman should stop panning. The dancers should then be allowed to dance within this steady frame, until they once more move into the right- or left-hand thirds of the picture and *push* the cameraman into another pan.

This technique renders camera movement quite unobtrusive, and the principle can be adapted to suit all ballet routines.

It is most important for the cameraman to memorize the movements that the dancers will make in every one of his shots. Whenever possible, he should allow the dancers to perform within a steady frame—panning only when he must.

He should imagine that the camera *wants* to stay central and static; and he should pan only when the artists "push" the edges

136

of his frame to left or right. This is the best way to avoid "nervy" camerawork—the sort of effect one gets when the cameraman pans in a series of nervous twitches every time the dancers move away from their central positions.

Although we are discussing panning only here, it is worth remembering that as the dancers move away from a high camera, they will also move towards the top of the framed shot. The cameraman should tilt up as the dancers move away from him, therefore, and tilt down as they approach him, in order to maintain correct headroom.

The Whip Pan

Occasionally—but only occasionally—the cameraman may be called upon to execute what is known as a "whip pan". This consists of panning the camera very quickly from one static shot to another, all detail on the screen becoming blurred during the pan by the speed of the movement. If used prudently, the whip pan can be very effective. It represents one of the rare occasions when camera movement is made deliberately obtrusive.

But it is a very specialized operation, and has to be used sparingly as a sort of shock effect. Some television directors overcome the technical difficulties of a whip pan by adapting a method used in film-making.

They instruct the cameraman to whip pan across a scene, but cut to the next static shot on another camera before the pan has ceased. The intention is to give the impression that this is one movement on one camera. Although this technique makes the cameraman's job very much easier, it is never as successful as a genuine whip pan.

The whip pan can be used to good effect in dramatic situations. A young girl is alone in an empty house. She hears a noise, and the director cuts to a close-up of her terrified face. She looks to her right and screams. In less than half a second the camera "whips" across the room in the direction of her gaze, and ends up on a close-up of the sneering villain. The girl screams again, out of shot, and the picture fades to black—leaving the viewer on the edge of his seat . . . or so the director hopes.

But it is the cameraman who has to perform this difficult movement. And to be successful, it *must* be well done. The whole dramatic effect is lost if the camera pans past the villain, or misses him altogether, or finishes up out of focus.

It would be far better for the director to drop the device altogether, than risk the ruination of a climax because of a badly performed whip pan.

No cameraman, because of lack of skill and technique, should force a director into such a move. The director has the right to expect his cameramen to be able to perform all aspects of camerawork—including the difficult whip pan. And it is an admission of incompetence if the cameraman cannot oblige.

The whip pan is difficult to do well. There is no time for second thoughts once the new subject is framed, and any correction of framing at this stage detracts from the effect.

Once again the answer is to practise; there is no substitute. When practising, the pan should be carried out slowly at first, so that the cameraman can get the feel of the distance through which he will have to move the camera. He should pay careful attention to the position of his body, and always stand so that he is comfortably placed for the end of the movement, as mentioned earlier in this chapter. This is the time to check, too, whether any refocusing or tilting is needed in order to frame the new subject correctly. If such corrections are necessary, they will have to be performed *during* the pan. Remember, if the subjects at the start and end of the pan are at different distances from the camera, refocusing may be unavoidable, and any obvious readjustments on the new shot will kill the impact of the whip pan.

As the cameraman practises this movement, speeding up the operation each time, he will find that he is panning, tilting, and refocusing instinctively. He should continue to practise until he can whip pan to the new subject with complete ease and confidence.

Then he should move his camera away to another area, before coming back quickly for the beginning of his whip pan and checking that he can still perform the operation flawlessly. This is how it will have to be when the programme is "on the air", and then there will be no second chances.

When the whip pan is performed well it is an exciting and effective device. If it fails then the cameraman is solely to blame—provided, of course, that the artists have taken up their rehearsed positions.

Tilting

Most of the rules for panning apply equally to tilting; and both moves are usually performed to direct the viewer's attention to some new point of interest.

138

Tilting on static subjects is generally done with a narrow-angle lens, in order to show detail to the viewer. A typical example is the tilt from a fashion model's head to her feet, to illustrate features of the outfit she is wearing.

The viewer needs to have time to assimilate the details of the subject, and for that reason the cameraman must pay close attention to the speed of the movement.

Remember, too, that the subject is closest to the camera during a tilt when the camera is pointing horizontally. If the tilt starts with the camera pointing up, and ends with it pointing down—as is usually the case—then refocusing will probably be necessary if a narrow-angle lens is used. The cameraman will have to focus towards him as he tilts down to the horizontal level; and away from him again as the tilt continues downwards. The degree of correction needed may be slight—but if it is necessary in order to maintain a sharp picture, then it must be carried out.

Static Scenes

If the cameraman is required to tilt up or down some such subject as a map, or a page of newspaper mounted as a caption, then it is worth checking first of all whether any panning will also be necessary during the movement. If not, then it is a good idea to lock the pan control on the panning head. The cameraman can then devote his full attention to the mechanics of tilting, with greater certainty of a smooth, regular movement, through knowing that the lens cannot wander from side to side while he is doing so.

When tilting has to be performed over a big vertical angle, there may be some difficulty in watching his viewfinder closely throughout the movement. Here again—as with panning—the cameraman should set himself and the viewfinder to be right for the *end* of the tilt. Most viewfinders, or viewfinder hoods—some more than others—are adjustable to allow for this. Often it is possible for the cameraman to use his head to move the viewfinder (or its hood) up or down while he is tilting.

But if he is doubtful whether he can manage to do this successfully during a long tilt, then he should set the viewfinder for the *end* of the tilt, and plan the movement backwards from that point.

Moving Artists

Tilting with an artist as he begins a move is fraught with danger.

If an artist is to stand up from a sitting position, the cameraman must take great care in covering the movement. If he tilts too slowly, the artist's head will vanish out of the top of the picture, until the cameraman "catches up with him". Obviously, this is not good technique.

But tilting too soon, and moving ahead of the artist, is equally bad. This way, the startled viewer will almost certainly be presented with an unwanted shot of the boom microphone!

The cameraman must concentrate carefully when preparing to tilt in these circumstances. There is always some indication that an artist is about to get up from a chair. He will lean .forward,

Fig. 55. The cameraman was not concentrating during this movement. He started too late and allowed the artist to move out of the top of frame. Then, in his hurry to catch up, he tilted too far and revealed the boom microphone.

put his hands on his knees—or on the arms of the chair if it has them—and sometimes move his feet. This may all sound very obvious, but it is surprising how often these clues are ignored in the "heat of the moment". The cameraman should be on the lookout for these warnings that an artist is about to rise.

He must tilt up *as soon as the artist starts to rise*, and *not* as he makes his first move forward in the chair. Leaning forward brings the head lower in frame, and to tilt up then would be fatal. Remember the ever-present microphone, hovering just above the top of the cameraman's shot.

The speed of the tilt is governed, of course, by the speed of the artist's movement. Inexperienced performers invariably tend to move far too quickly. It is the director's job to warn them to avoid doing so. But if the cameraman finds that he cannot cover the movement smoothly, even when their speed has been reduced, he should point this out to the director. Artist movements such as these must be performed quite slowly in front of the camera, and it is better to correct this at the outset than risk a hurried and untidy movement.

It is worth remembering that if a seated artist is held in a tight shot, refocusing may be necessary as he leans forward prior to getting up. As he completes the move, too, further adjustment of focus may be necessary.

Tilting with an artist from a standing position to a sitting position has its problems, too. Remember that people tend to sit down a little faster than they stand up. They also tend to lower their heads considerably while they are in the process of sitting, and then raise them suddenly as they settle into a sitting position.

If the shot is held fairly wide, this bobbing of the head can be ignored, and the camera movement can consist of a steady, downward tilt. But if the shot is no wider than a mid-shot, it may be necessary to follow this lowering and raising of the head. And again refocusing may be needed.

It is very difficult to tilt smoothly with an artist who is moving slowly down a flight of stairs, one step at a time. This sort of action is common in musical shows. The singer takes eight lines of a song to walk down eight steps, moving elegantly, and pausing for a second on each step.

To follow this movement in a series of individual tilts can be ugly and distracting. But the slow speed of the artist makes a steady tilt unsuitable. Often, the best method is to tilt in a series of steps, slowing the speed of the tilt towards the end of each movement so that it runs into the beginning of the next tilt.

That may sound a little complicated, but if the move is practised the effect will become quite clear. The camera never stops moving and the headroom is kept steady.

Tilt with Pan

Tilting is often combined with panning, and the cameraman should strive to ensure that these two movements appear as one. To pan along part of a scene, then tilt a little, then continue to pan and so on, is bad technique. As mentioned earlier, a steady diagonal progression is the aim. An uneasy "marriage" between

142

panning and tilting makes the camera movement obtrusive, and this must be avoided whenever possible.

The earliest forms of camera movement that the trainee will be called upon to perform are panning and tilting. He must learn to do them well—and that means unobtrusively—before he attempts the more involved manoeuvres described in the following chapters.

11

TRACKING AND CRABBING

OF all forms of camera movement, tracking is the most difficult to do well. Bad technique in tracking is disturbing and obvious. The cameraman, if he is to succeed in his profession, must master the complexities of this form of camera movement, and devote as much time as possible to perfecting it.

There are so many things a cameraman must think about when tracking, and so many things he must do simultaneously to make the operation a complete success. The movement must be smooth, as unobtrusive as possible, and logical. To be logical, there must be a reason or motivation for the track—as discussed earlier—and the object of the track should never be in doubt.

The Object of Tracking

How often have we seen a camera tracking in from a wide shot of a group of people, and seeming to be in doubt until the last second just who to single out as the "target" for the track?

We may be left in doubt because the camera is swaying from side to side as it moves forward, centring first on one person, and then another, as it shudders its way into the set.

In a bad track, the first part of the manoeuvre is often performed as if the camera is locked, with no attempt made to favour a particular artist. Then, when the camera is close enough to see who is who, it veers to right or left and settles on its final framing.

This is bad camerawork. The cameraman must know before he starts to track who, or what, he is going to frame in his final shot. He must also be able to perform the movement smoothly and progressively. And he must avoid losing focus during the track.

It is worth spending some time on this subject of tracking. Performed badly, tracking can be an eyesore. Performed well, it is a pleasure to watch. The viewer—the ever-present viewer—

144

must be kept interested and entertained. He may not be aware of the niceties of tracking, but he will be unsettled—if only sub-consciously—if his picture sways and trembles and becomes diffused before his eyes.

The director, too, will not be amused by bad technique in tracking. So often the dramatic effect of a track is lost if the cameraman hunts for focus at the end of a wild, shuddering move. All too obvious can be the results of such accidents as tracking the camera dolly into pieces of furniture, hitting the boom, or running over cables. They appear on the screen as violent upheavals—often accompanied by appropriate sound effects! And it is usually the cameraman who is to blame.

Although such accidents occasionally happen to us all, they are generally the result of carelessness.

Forgetting to set the dolly for the line of a track has been mentioned earlier. This particular mistake is elementary, and the effect is obvious to the lay-man. But there is far more to tracking than that, as the would-be cameraman soon finds out.

Early experiences of this form of movement are normally con-fined to working with a pedestal dolly. Operating a camera mounted on a manually-tracked dolly, motorized dolly, or motorized crane, will come later in the cameraman's professional life. When tracking with a pedestal he is on his own. He has no one to blame but himself if anything goes wrong.

But tracking with a pedestal teaches, above all, camera control and speed of movement. It provides the basis of a technique which must be instinctive by the time the cameraman is called upon to operate a camera mounted on larger dollies. Then he will have to control his trackers by hand signals. But if he can master the technique of tracking with a pedestal, the cameraman will almost certainly produce good work when he is in control of the track-ing on more complicated dollies.

"You can judge a cameraman by his tracking." If that is not a television proverb, it should be!

It goes without saying by now that the panning head and the dolly must be in good adjustment, and set ready for the track.

Keeping the camera steady during the track is essential. But it is no less vital than holding focus, which we shall discuss shortly.

Most cameramen develop their own "driving techniques", to achieve maximum stability during tracking. These depend both on the individual cameraman and on the make of camera being operated. With some types it is possible to brace the forearm along

145

the side of the camera, and some cameramen also press their foreheads against the viewfinder hood. The exact method is not important. But the results are.

Focusing

Focusing provides the cameraman with more headaches than any other feature of tracking. As we know, if the camera is moved closer to a subject, or if the subject moves towards the camera, refocusing is necessary as soon as the subject begins to move out of the depth of field.

Refocusing is achieved on a television camera either by moving the tube in relation to the lens, or the lens in relation to the tube. The focusing mechanism consists of a handle, wheel, capstan, or similar device mounted on one side of the camera. By moving this device one way or the other, the cameraman can focus on near or far subjects. As we know, when he moves the focusing device to pick out subjects far from the lens, we say he is "focusing back". If he focuses on subjects near the lens, he is "focusing forward".

If we focus on an artist in long-shot, and then track in until the artist is in close-up, we must "focus forward" during the track. But the amount of refocusing needed depends on many things: the focal length of the lens, for one. If a wide-angle lens (that is, a lens of short focal length) is being used, less adjustment of focus will be necessary than with a narrow-angle lens (that is, a lens of long focal length).

The distance to be travelled by the camera is relevant, too. Clearly, if the camera starts the track a great distance from the subject and tracks in to a close-up of the face, as in the above example, more refocusing will be necessary than if a track covers only a few feet.

The aperture, or stop, at which the lens is set is also important here. There is less depth of field at $f\,5{\cdot}6$ than at $f\,11$ and therefore the margin for error is reduced.

But what makes focusing so difficult is the fact that the correction which the cameraman must make while tracking is not regular throughout the track.

Take the above example. If the cameraman is using a 25-degree lens, he will find that no refocusing is necessary for the first two or three feet of the track. As he goes closer, however, he will have to turn the focusing device and "focus forward" progressively more and more. During the last foot or two of the track—as he moves in from a mid-shot to a close-up of his subject—the cameraman will

146

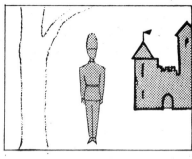

Fig. 56. Focused back—the castle only is sharp.

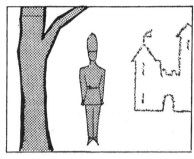

Focused forward—the tree is the sharpest point.

Correct focus—the soldier, who is the centre of interest, is the object of focus.

have to move the focusing device more than he has done for the whole of the distance already covered.

The cameraman does not turn the focusing device an equal amount for a given distance travelled towards or away from a subject. For a cameraman tracking in towards a subject, the closer he goes, the more he has to refocus. And the opposite is, of course, true of tracking out.

This is because, for a given lens, as the camera moves closer to the subject, so the depth of field decreases. From a depth of field of ten feet or so at the start of the track, the cameraman may have only a couple of inches of depth of field at the finish of the movement. There is virtually no margin for error when the camera has

147

moved really close to a subject. And yet that is when correct focus is of paramount importance.

Only when the lens is focused at the hyperfocal distance will the camera be sufficiently focused over most of the scene. Otherwise we have to continually focus for maximum sharpness, as the subject distance varies.

There are two fundamental approaches to focusing in the photographic camera: either by examining a ground-glass image, or by carefully measured distances, knowing one's aperture and the relative depth-of-field obtained. Film camerawork often uses the second system, the viewfinder being used to determine shot coverage alone. The "focus-puller" continually adjusts the lens' focusing distance as the camera tracks. In the television camera, however, the cameraman watching a television image, controls his own focus adjustment and directs and moves his camera at the same time. With a pedestal mounting he does all this entirely unaided.

It is hardly surprising then, that even the most experienced and adroit TV cameraman has his bad moments or loses focus on rare occasions.

But this knowledge may not make him feel very much better when the director comments: "Thank you, Camera Three. That was fine at the beginning and end of the track, but I think we got a little lost in the middle, didn't we?" Such things happen!

The best advice, as has been repeated so many times before, is to practise. The cameraman should spend any free time he has on the studio floor practising. He should track in and out on anything in sight. Short tracks, long tracks, fast tracks, slow tracks; all should be attempted again and again. Only after hours spent at this will the cameraman begin to get the feel of the amount of focus correction needed in any given situation.

He should also practise tracking on different lenses. As we shall see later, tracking is best attempted on lenses with an acceptance angle of 20 degrees or more. But the cameraman may sometimes have to track with a lens of a narrower angle.

When to Refocus

When tracking, it is not a good idea to try to guess or calculate the amount of focus correction needed as the movement progresses, and turn the focusing device accordingly. If the cameraman then loses focus during the track, he will have given himself another problem to cope with. He has lost focus; but is this because he has focused too far forward, or too far back?

He has to make up his mind about this quickly. He is moving all the time, and cannot stop to work it out. Occasionally, something will give him a clue. The artist is out of focus, but the set behind is sharp. He has therefore focused too far back, and must focus forward immediately.

But more often than not he will have no way of knowing. He has no option but to move the focusing device one way or the other. But if he has already focused too far forward, and focuses farther forward in trying to find out where he is, this will make the situation even worse. And since he will still be moving the camera at the same time anyway, by the time he has found focus he will have lost the feel of the track. This way lies disaster!

The better method is to do no focusing during the track *until the picture just starts to "go soft"*. The definition on the cameraman's viewfinder is far superior to that on the viewer's set at home. The cameraman sees when a picture starts to "go soft" long before the viewer will notice it, and he can use this fact to his advantage. This can best be explained by an example.

Let us assume that the cameraman is tracking in. The artist is in long-shot, and the track will take us into a close-up. The cameraman should watch his viewfinder very carefully. For the first few feet of the track, as we know, no focusing will be necessary. But from then on the picture will start to "go soft", unless the cameraman focuses forward progressively. He must watch for the first signs that the picture is going out of focus, and then focus forward, gently, to compensate.

And he must do this throughout the track—"chasing focus" all the time, yet only the smallest fraction of an inch behind. He will know, should he lose focus, that he has not been correcting fast enough. There can be only one way to remedy this—by focusing forward. This way the cameraman has no need to guess or experiment—he *knows*.

This is the safest and most widely used method of overcoming the focus problem, and the trainee cameraman is advised to stick to it. Eventually, experience with this method will give him an instinct for focusing that will be valuable in any situation.

It seems to be far more difficult to hold focus while tracking out, than while tracking in. When tracking out, of course, the greatest correction of focus is needed at the beginning of the track. And the correction becomes progressively less as the track proceeds.

This fact seems to be psychologically alien to the average cameraman, who is usually happier when the correction needed

149

increases as the track progresses. Even greater care is needed, therefore, when tracking out from a subject. This is particularly true if the camera starts its track from a position very close to the subject—as is often the case.

Focusing Point

It might help the struggling cameraman to point out that it is in his own interests to concentrate on the minimum amount of detail in his shot when wrestling with the problems of focusing. Let us imagine that he is tracking in from a long shot to a close-up of an artist. For the first part of the movement the cameraman should single out some item of clothing that provides a reliable focusing aid—a striped shirt, or lace stole, for example. He should shut his mind to the other elements of the scene (from a focusing point of view) and glue his eyes to the item he has selected.

As he reaches a mid-shot, or thereabouts, he should switch his attention to the eyes of the artist, and use them as his main points of focus until the end of the track—the close-up. If the cameraman mentally roams over the scene to check that all is well from a focusing standpoint he will soon become confused. He must settle on one part of the subject until the eyes can be seen, and thereafter concentrate on them entirely.

Static Scene Focusing

One of the most difficult problems in focusing crops up when a cameraman is called upon to track out from, or in to, a photograph or a caption. Here the "target" for the track is a two-dimensional object. It is all in one plane, and has no depth. During the track, it is either in focus or it is not. There can be no half measures.

Also, since subjects of this sort are invariably small in size compared with the size of a set or an artist, the camera movement takes place very close to them. There is practically no depth of field, therefore, and no margin for error.

A further complication is that tracking in to a photograph may well have to be performed with a lens of a comparatively narrow angle of view. This is because the camera would have to go so close to the subject on a wide-angle lens that it would be impossible to direct any light on to it.

Although the depth of field is virtually unaffected whatever lens is used in this case—since the subject framing is constant—more movement of the focusing mechanism is necessary the narrower the angle of view of the lens unless the design incorporates mechanical compensation.

Further, as we shall examine in greater detail later, tracking with a narrow-angle lens is usually unsatisfactory. Any flaws in camera movement are more easily detected, because they are exaggerated. Smooth tracking on a narrow-angle lens is almost impossible. But when the subject is a photograph or caption on a stand the cameraman often has no option: he must grit his teeth and make the best of it.

Of course, if the photograph or picture itself is not of good quality, or is slightly out of focus, the cameraman cannot hope to have anything but a poor quality, out-of-focus picture to frame during the track. This makes his track even more difficult, for it will be impossible for him to be really sure at any time whether or not he is holding focus. His only hope in these circumstances is to try to find a part of the photograph or picture that is sharp, and keep his eyes glued to this spot during the track. This is where the zoom lens comes into its own, for size-changes by zooming are simplicity itself on captions. Once zoom-focus has been adjusted for maximum sharpness it remains, however we zoom.

There is no easy way to overcome the problems of a track of this sort. Once again, practice is the only answer. After a dozen or so attempts, a certain feeling is developed for the movement, and the cameraman will have to rely on this when he is called upon to carry out this particular manoeuvre "on the air".

Tracking out from these two-dimensional subjects is twice as difficult as tracking in. But either way, it is such a tricky operation that some cameramen never do master it. Some, with an indefinable flair, seem to find it much easier than others; and they are the envy of their colleagues.

Once a cameraman feels that he has mastered the focusing problem, he would be well advised not to become obsessed by it when tracking. With sufficient experience it usually looks after itself. Provided he has attained a degree of skill in focusing, the cameraman will find that if he concentrates on the other mechanics of tracking, which we shall look at later, he focuses more or less automatically while moving the camera, and the problem is solved.

Lenses for Tracking

Whenever possible wide-angle lenses (that is lenses of short focal length) should be used for tracking. There are a number of reasons for this.

In the first place, flaws in camera movement—such as slight

shaking of the dolly due to irregularities in the floor—show up less on these lenses than on the narrow-angle lenses. When using lenses with a horizontal angle of view of less than about 20 degrees, it is virtually impossible to perform smooth, unobtrusive camera movement. This is no reflection on the cameraman's ability. It is simply due to the nature of the long-focus lens which was not, in any case, intended for tracking, but primarily for picking up close-up shots at a distance from the subject.

Secondly, a greater feeling of movement is imparted with a wide-angle lens. As we saw earlier, narrow-angle lenses tend to foreshorten distance. Distant objects do not appear very much smaller than objects close to the lens, and there is little sense of perspective. This has an effect on the feeling of movement during a track as the following example will show.

A cameraman, using a 24-degree lens, frames an artist in long-shot. He places the artist's feet at the bottom of the frame. If he then tracks the camera towards the artist for a distance of about six feet, the artist's knees are now at the bottom of the frame.

If the original long shot is taken with a lens of 9 degrees, however, and the camera tracked in for the same distance, only the artist's ankles are reached at the bottom of the frame. This time there appears to be no appreciable movement towards the artist; and yet the camera has moved the same distance towards him in each case.

In addition to this, the use of the 9-degree lens makes the track unsteady and distracting. Narrow-angle lenses have their function in television—but they are not suitable for tracking!

A word of warning is also needed, however, about the use of wide-angle lenses. They tend to make near objects appear large, and distant objects small. This gives an exaggerated impression of perspective, but it is not always an advantage.

If the lens is tracked close to an artist's face, for example, it can cause unflattering distortion. The nose, because it is nearest the camera, appears large in relation to the rest of the face; or if the close-up is taken from a position below the level of the artist's face, the chin looms large and heavy in foreground. No artist will thank the cameraman for doing that to him—and female performers are entitled to have hysterics if they see the result on a monitor!

This effect is most noticeable on the very wide angle lenses—those with an angle of 45 degrees and more. But it can also be a danger when the usual studio wide-angle lens of about 36 degrees is used. Whenever possible, tracking in to a close-up of an artist's face should be carried out on the normal, 24-degree lens.

Pivoting and Tracking

When a camera is tracked in, the purpose is normally to isolate a particular person or thing. The director wants the viewer to be taken closer to the object. He has something to show him, and he has decided to achieve this by means of a forward movement on one camera.

Imagine three men standing shoulder to shoulder, and framed in the cameraman's shot, with the camera at its normal height. The bottom of the frame runs through their waists, and the elbows of the outside men touch the left- and right-hand edges of the picture. If the pan and tilt controls on the panning head are then firmly locked, and the camera tracked right in, we shall probably end up with a close shot of the centre man's tie.

If we want the camera to end up on a close-up of the centre man's face, however, it will be necessary for the cameraman to tilt up slightly as he is tracking in. In doing so, he should not increase the headroom. But he should regard the top of the frame as a hinge, and pivot his picture about that line as he tracks in.

His intention, when tilting as he tracks in, is to prevent the picture "closing in" from the top of the frame at the same speed at which it is closing in from the other three sides. He will allow the headroom to decrease slightly as he moves in from a three-shot to a close-up, of course. But the outside men will vanish rapidly out of the sides of the picture, and the bottom of frame will move up the centre man's body until it is in the right position for a close-up.

We refer to this method of holding some parts of the frame steady while hinging on others as pivoting. Tracking invariably entails some degree of pivoting. Very often the pivoting is varied three or four times during a track, in order to get the desired effect.

When the cameraman pivots about the left-hand side of the frame, this means that as he tracks he pans to the left throughout in sympathy with the speed of the track. His aim is to keep the distance between the artist and the left of frame constant throughout the movement.

Pivoting provides the quickest, most pleasing and smoothest means of isolating the object of a track.

Let us imagine that the cameraman has framed a two-shot. The

153

Fig. 57. If we track in from this three-shot with the panning head locked . . .

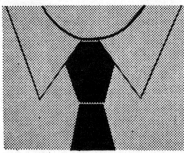

. . . we shall end on a C.U. of the centre man's tie.

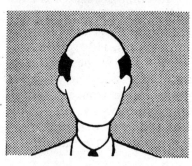

If we want to end on a C.U. of the centre man, we must pivot about the top of frame during the track.

two people are sitting in chairs, half facing each other and half facing the camera. They have been holding a discussion and have come to the end of their item. The director instructs the cameraman to track in to the left-hand artist, who will close the discussion and introduce the next item.

It is extremely bad technique in these circumstances to pan to the left, centre-up the left-hand artist, and track in. The cameraman should pivot on his left-hand side of frame—and the top of frame too—as he tracks in. By doing this the cameraman will quickly lose the right-hand artist, who will vanish out of the right-hand side of the frame. The final framing of the left-hand artist is then a simple, smooth operation.

154

Fig. 58. If we are to track in from this two-shot to the man . . .

. . . we must pivot mainly about the left-hand edge of frame, and allow the woman to vanish unnoticed out of the right of frame . . .

. . . and complete the track as here.

We should *not* pan to the left at the beginning of the track and place the man in the centre of frame, and then continue the track, keeping him centrally framed throughout the movement until the final shot is formed.

155

That is an elementary example of the need for pivoting, which must be employed to greater or lesser extent, during all tracks. The cameraman must allow all detail which is not included in his final framing to exit as soon as possible from his shot, and pivot accordingly.

In the example just quoted, if the artist turns towards the camera as it moves in, a neater track is possible if the cameraman tracks diagonally in to the artist. This will help the cameraman to pivot smoothly, and enable him to perform a neat track. The result will be a smooth, gliding progression from two-shot to close-up.

The direction of the track will be on a line drawn from the position of the camera for the two-shot, to its position for the close-up. The cameraman must set his dolly for this line before the track. If he has any doubt about the start and finishing points of his track, he should mark them on the studio floor with crayon.

In fact, the cameraman must always study the best line for any given track. In many cases, a track up or down the centre line of a set will not be as good as a diagonal move.

During most long tracks the cameraman will find that he must continually change the edges of frame about which he is pivoting.

We can take as an example a pianist who is sitting at a concert grand piano. The cameraman can frame a pleasing long shot if he places his camera at an angle of approximately 45 degrees to the keyboard. In this shot the pianist's back will probably be just inside the left-hand edge of frame, and the far end of the piano will be near the right-hand edge of frame. The legs of the piano will almost stand on the bottom of the picture. When the cameraman is asked to track into a close-up of the artist's hands he must vary his pivoting at different stages during the track.

For the first part of the movement, he should pivot about the left-hand edge and the bottom of the frame simultaneously. In other words he must keep the distance between the artist's back and the left-hand edge of frame constant, holding the legs of the piano near the bottom of frame. The picture will now close in from the top and the right-hand side of the frame.

Once he is satisfied that the headroom is correct for a medium long shot, the cameraman should then pivot about the top and the left-hand edges of frame, and allow the picture to close in from the right-hand side and the bottom of the frame together.

He should continue to do this until the pianist is framed in a mid-shot, his back still just inside the left-hand edge of frame.

Fig. 59. The cameraman has framed this attractive L.S. and is instructed to track in to the pianist's hands. For the first part of the movement he should pivot mainly about the left-hand edge and bottom of frame until . . .

. . . this framing has been reached. He should then pivot mainly about the left-hand edge and top of frame until . . .

. . . the right-hand edge and bottom of frame have closed in to here. He should then pivot mainly about the bottom of frame—and partly about the right-hand edge until . . .

. . . the hands are seen in relation to almost the whole of the keyboard. Then it is a simple operation to frame a C.U. of the hands.

The keyboard will run to the right-hand edge of the shot, and his knees will rest on the bottom of the picture.

The cameraman should now pivot about the right-hand side and bottom of the frame, when the picture will close in towards the hands. The final centring of these hands will then be a simple matter.

All that may sound a little complicated. But if the cameraman experiments with the method after reading it carefully, the meaning should be quite clear. It is not a simple and straightforward movement: but camerawork seldom is.

There is no doubt, however, that if the cameraman can master this technique of pivoting, as illustrated above, he can be relied upon to perform artistic and technically competent tracks.

All tracking will require pivoting in one form or another. The cameraman must decide *before* he starts the movement which edges of the frame he will pivot about, and when he will change them during the track. He must watch the edges of frame like a hawk.

Where he has decided that the distance between a subject and the edge of frame shall remain constant, he should concentrate carefully on that distance, and never allow it to vary. On no account must he let the camera sway as he tracks and reveal extra details of the picture, which have then to be excluded. This is extremely bad technique.

Where a singer, for example, is held in the right-hand side of frame, there is often a piece of scenery in the left-hand foreground. As the cameraman tracks in, he should pivot about the right-hand edge of the frame so that the left-hand foreground object will be lost from his picture first, and then vary his framing to end up on the shot he had in mind. It is far more difficult to pivot successfully when tracking out than when tracking in, and the cameraman must concentrate hard in these circumstances if he is to produce a smooth, pleasing track.

Many examples of the art of pivoting could be given, but a careful study of an evening's television will provide the cameraman with many instances of this technique. Unfortunately, he will also see examples of bad tracking, but there is nothing like a bad example to inspire good intentions.

Tracking in Sympathy with Mood

The speed of one track will not necessarily be the speed of another: this is obvious. Sometimes the action will require a fast track, sometimes a track which is so slow as to be almost

Fig. 60. The cameraman has pivoted mainly about the right-hand edge of frame throughout the track. The transition from L.S. to M.S. has been accomplished in an artistic and unobtrusive manner.

imperceptible—it is really the director who decides this. But if the cameraman understands the effect that the director is trying to achieve, he can play a major part in making the operation a success.

Tracking to music is a good example of the need to pay attention to tracking speeds. Obviously, twenty-mile-an-hour tracks, even if they were possible, would be quite out of place if they were directed at a tear-stained artist who was singing *Home Sweet Home*. The mood would be shattered. Pathos would be reduced to farce.

But the principle can be applied in more subtle ways. The speed of a track should fit in with the mood of the particular piece of music. And wherever possible the track should start at the beginning of a verse or passage, and stop when it ends. During very slow passages of music, the effect obtained by a correspondingly slow track can be quite dramatic—even exciting.

The cameraman should start the track as the singer takes a breath prior to singing. Psychologically it is right. Artistically it is right. And technically, it provides an unvariable cue for the start of the movement.

During fast passages of music, fast tracks might, of course, take place during parts of verses. They will rarely last for the whole

159

of a verse or passage. But the track should be timed to start at the beginning of a line, or phrase, and finish at the end of another. Some cameramen have an inborn feeling for this technique, but artistic tracks are possible from even the tone-deaf cameraman.

Cameramen must remember that during long, slow tracks, any camera shake or sway is an intrusion. The cameraman must concentrate on holding his camera as steady as possible. Focusing is usually a relatively simple matter in these circumstances.

Some cameramen, when confronted with extremely slow and dramatic tracks, use the following method (we are, of course, dealing only with pedestal dollies at this stage). They wrap their focusing arm around the camera, and press their heads against the viewfinder hood. They then place one foot on the pedestal base, and tuck the panning handle under the armpit. The camera is now firmly held, yet still under control.

They then propel the dolly forward by "walking" with the heel and the ball of the foot which is still in contact with the floor. This foot must never leave the floor, of course!

But tracking to music is not the only time that the cameraman must pay special attention to the speed and manner of his tracks. In plays, for example, the mood of the action will call for different approaches. If the cameraman thinks about *why* he is tracking, and attempts to capture the mood for himself, he is half-way to a successful track. What is just as important, it will also reflect the director's intentions.

Very fast tracks are often called for to heighten a dramatic situation, and the cameraman can ruin the desired effect if his technique is bad. He must do his best to minimize camera shake—always a danger during fast tracks—and he must pivot carefully, however fast he is moving. Finally—and just as important as the other points mentioned—he must hold focus.

As with the whip pan, nothing can kill a dramatic effect more than the cameraman hunting for focus at the end of a fast movement. It is not easy to hold focus in these circumstances, particularly if the camera ends up very close to the subject. But it must be done. The track is less than worthless if it is ruined by bad camerawork.

Slow tracks in dramatic situations should receive the same care as those during poignant musical items. It should be clear in the cameraman's mind exactly when he is going to start the track. He must know when, dramatically, it should end. And he should govern the speed of the track to conform with this.

Above all, he must keep unnecessary camera movement down to a minimum. He must watch the edges of his frame carefully, too, pivoting as if the sides of his frame were on hinges. And he must move as quietly as possible during quiet passages of dialogue.

Some cameramen find difficulty in tracking with artists who are moving towards or away from the camera. If he intends to keep the artist in the same size shot during the track, the cameraman must synchronize the speed of his camera movement with the speed of the artist.

But that is easier said than done. Not every artist can be guaranteed to move at a regular speed throughout a movement. Singers, in particular, like to pause now and then while demonstrating the quality of their top notes. This is understandable: it is professional staging. But it does not make for a smooth, even track.

If the pauses are short, the cameraman should slow the track just before the pause, then run on into the next movement when the pause is over. This is rather similar to the technique of tilting with an artist who is moving up or down a staircase.

The cameraman must be careful to hold focus, too. No refocusing will be necessary if the artist is held in the same size shot during the movement. But when one gets ahead of the other some adjustment of focus may be necessary. It depends on the lens being used, and the distance from the camera to the artist.

As a final word of advice on this subject, be very careful not to dip the camera at the beginning and end of a track. This often happens when the cameraman is tracking with a pedestal dolly. The pressure he exerts to start the dolly rolling—and to stop it at the end of the track—can be transmitted to the camera. This results in the camera bobbing up and down, and it is an indication that the cameraman lacks experience.

Cameramen who are inexperienced in the operation of cameras mounted on mechanized dollies are guilty of this too. The trackers never seem to start the track exactly on cue, and when they do move off the cameraman is caught napping. We shall be dealing with this in greater detail in a later chapter.

Before leaving the subject of tracking for a while, it is worth repeating the importance of this aspect of camerawork. The cameraman will never be wasting his time if he practises tracking at every opportunity. He must master the technique before he can call himself a cameraman at all. But if he strives to perfect the niceties of tracking; if he can lose focus less often than anyone

161

else; if he can pivot with no swaying or shaking; then he will be an asset to any team.

Crabbing

Most of the basic, general principles which govern the technique of successful camera movement apply to crabbing.

As we know, crabbing is movement of the camera across a scene, parallel to it. This can be a very exciting operation to look at from the viewer's point of view. If there are trees, people, pieces of scenery, etc., in foreground, they appear to rush past the lens. The viewer is conscious of an acute feeling of "presence". He is there: the trees are almost brushing his face.

This form of crabbing is not a difficult operation for the cameraman to perform. Most cameramen like crabbing when it is straightforward. It is comparatively easy to do well, yet the effect can be exciting and dramatic.

But crabbing is often combined with tracking to produce a circular movement about a scene, and this is not an easy operation at all.

The cameraman must still concentrate on smooth movement, pivoting, focusing and pleasing framing. At the same time he must try to avoid tripping over his own feet and keep a watchful eye on his camera cable.

When crabs of this nature are called for, the cameraman should endeavour to get someone to help him perform the manoeuvre. It is extremely difficult to push a pedestal dolly in a sideways direction, and at the same time keep the camera steady and pointing in the right line.

Shaky crabs are all too common, and the cameraman will find that it is well worth his while to master the correct technique.

We have looked at the four basic forms of camera movement. Often they must all be performed simultaneously as one manoeuvre. No cameraman can attempt such an operation unless he has already mastered the individual techniques of each, and that is why he is urged to practise these at every opportunity. He must perform all forms of camera movement smoothly and instinctively. He cannot do this simply by reading and watching—he must get hold of his camera and try for himself: there is no other way.

162

12

OTHER CAMERA MOVEMENTS

MOST studio pedestal dollies have a central column which can be raised or lowered quite easily. Mechanized dollies are invariably equipped with some means of varying the height of the camera. These facilities offer an extra dimension to the cameraman, but he must understand the implications of varying the height of the camera if he is to exploit this additional medium to the full.

Varying the Height

Cameramen must not fall into the habit of setting a pedestal dolly at a comfortable working height, and then leaving it there throughout a whole programme. It is so easy for a trainee cameraman to develop this frame of mind during his early days of coping with framing, focusing, tracking, and so on. He might well think that the height of his camera is the least important of his worries. But it is not.

The height of a camera in relation to a scene is something that must be considered with each new shot the cameraman takes. Changes in camera height can affect the mood of a shot, for example. And varying the height of the camera during a shot needs the careful thought and treatment that is given to a track or a crab.

Before looking at the basic problems of height variations during a shot, we must first consider the effect on a picture of high and low positions of the camera. We discussed the results of different camera heights in earlier chapters, but we can treat the subject in greater detail here.

A low camera position tends to make foreground objects prominent. Persons and settings in the background of the picture sink lower in frame and become less significant. If an artist stands in foreground and he is shot from a low camera position, he dominates the scene. We look at him with awe: he is not to be taken lightly.

This low-angle shooting is often used in television drama, and it can heighten the effect of tense situations. The mood can be exaggerated if a low camera position is accompanied by dramatic lighting, taking care to avoid lens flares or shoot-off.

Conversely, high camera positions tend to bring background objects into prominence: foreground objects will appear less significant.

These variations of height have other effects too. A low-angle shot gives an impression of lack of space, and when a ceiling-piece is included as part of a set the effect can be almost claustrophobic.

High-angle shots—particularly when the subject is some distance from the camera—give a feeling of space and depth. These shots are particularly useful when the director wants us to feel that an aura of loneliness or detachment surrounds an artist.

Matching Heights

These were obvious examples of the need to pay attention to camera height. But every shot should be studied with the question of suitable camera height in mind. It is as important as deciding on the correct lens and camera position.

Take as an example the straightforward, two-shot interview. The basic set-up for this type of item is to place one camera at right-angles to the chairs, holding a two-shot, and two further cameras on each side of the central camera. These side cameras will be used for mid-shots, medium close-ups, and close-ups of the two artists respectively.

As mentioned in another chapter, it is important that lenses of the same angle of view should be used on cameras when matching shots. The cameras should also be equidistant from the particular artists they are shooting, and at similar angles to them.

But it is just as important that they are both at the same height. If one camera is shooting from a very low angle and the other from a very high angle, the difference between the types of shots each is taking will be quite marked.

But the effect is still there when smaller differences in height exist. It is sometimes a subtle matter: but it is important. Correct matching of shots such as these will never be entirely successful unless attention is paid to this aspect of correct camera height.

Using the Right Lens

When the director wishes to obtain the full effect of low- or high-angle camera positions, the cameraman should use his widest

164

angle lens. This will inevitably take the camera close to the artist, and the effect will be to increase the feeling of height, whether the camera is high or low.

Those parts of the artist nearest the camera will appear large. Those parts of him farther away will appear to have diminished rapidly in size. The brain will interpret this as an indication that the eye is looking at the subject from a very low or very high position, as the case may be. In fact it will assume that the camera is much lower or higher than it really is.

But it is worth repeating that care is needed in the use of wide-angle lenses when placed near artists. As we discussed earlier, they can cause unflattering distortion if taken too close to facial features. And this distortion is particularly marked when the shot is taken from low or high camera positions.

The cameraman should study an artist before deciding on the the height at which he will place his camera when taking a shot. If he thinks about this beforehand, he can avoid exaggerating imperfect features. And if he is very careful he can flatter artists with his shots by minimizing their facial and bodily flaws. Both male and female artists will love him for this. Most professional entertainers know their "best side". They will respect a cameraman who is conscious of this, and who always shoots them from a flattering angle.

This advice does not apply, of course, when it is the director's intention to exaggerate certain features for effect. Most of the rules of television are broken for effect, but that is the only occasion when they should be broken. It should never be due to the carelessness or incompetence of the cameraman.

Varying Height while Tracking

It is often necessary—or artistically desirable—to vary camera height when tracking. The best effects are obtained on trackable dollies and cranes, of which more will be said later. But some pedestal dollies are so designed and balanced that the cameraman can raise or lower the camera as he tracks. If he is using this type of pedestal, he should consider whether any track would benefit if he varied the height during the movement. If he thinks it would, then he should do so.

When using a pedestal dolly, it is very difficult for the cameraman to track if the camera is perched high on the central column. Really firm control over the camera cannot be guaranteed. The dolly, too, is less stable when the column is extended, and unevenness of the studio floor will be transmitted to the camera. The cameraman will also find it difficult to see the whole of his viewfinder picture throughout the movement.

In these circumstances he should be provided with a tracker to help him with his track. If possible he should climb on to the pedestal, and allow himself to be propelled by the tracker. If he is unable to get help he must do the best he can, but the track will then rarely be a complete success. This type of work is best left to cameras mounted on cranes and other trackable dollies.

The cameraman should consider the advantages to be gained by climbing on to the pedestal even for static shots. If he can place himself on the pedestal in such a way that there is no danger of his falling off, he will be far more successful with his high shots than if he stands on tip-toe, and peers into a half-visible viewfinder.

Aid to Composition

Varying camera height can aid composition. If an artist is sitting in such a position in a set that a mirror on the wall behind him appears to be standing on his head, this can be cured by shooting from a higher angle. The mirror will then move up in the frame, and its disturbing effect will be lessened. Similarly, if the top of a vase is just visible behind an artist's head, lowering the camera will hide the object.

Many examples of the application of camera height as an aid to composition could be given. But the principle is always the same. Shooting a subject from a higher position causes background objects to rise towards the top of the frame. Lowering the camera causes them to sink towards the bottom of the frame.

Zooming

Once having focused, we can go on zooming in and out, and the subject will always be perfectly in focus. But if the artist moves out of the depth of field during a zoom, the lens must be refocused *during* the zooming operation. This is not easy to achieve, and the amount of focus correction needed might be considerable if the artist is close to the camera, and a wide *f* stop is being used.

Zoom and Track

Cameramen are sometimes asked to zoom and track together. This is usually wanted by the director in order to give the impression of a long track, and it is often done at speed. The wide range of modern zoom lenses obviates the need for this hazardous, combined movement, but some studios are not equipped with

166

them. Despite the fact that zooming and tracking together cannot be recommended—because of the difficulty of guaranteeing the success of the operation—there is no doubt that a startling effect can be obtained with this manoeuvre.

But what of the cameraman? How is he to perform this difficult operation? Perhaps the following advice will be of some help.

If he is required to zoom and track out from a subject simultaneously, he should (after setting up the lens) perform the zooming part of the operation first. As he is nearing the end of the zoom, and coming to the widest angle it can accept, he should start tracking. He should then complete the zooming part of the operation during the first three or four feet of the track, and continue the movement as a straightforward track with a wide lens—the widest viewing angle of the zoom lens, in fact. And the wider the angle of view of the zoom lens, the easier and smoother the track.

Tracking and zooming in together entails using the same technique in reverse. The camera should be tracked in (with the lens set at its widest angle) until a predetermined point on the studio floor has been reached. At this point, the track should cease, and the rest of the operation carried out on the zoom lens only.

This is a particularly difficult feature of camerawork to master, and the cameraman is well advised to suggest another means of obtaining the same effect. But if the director wants it—he must be given it. The technique needs practice and care, though if the cameraman can make a success of the manoeuvre he will grow in stature.

Zoom and Pivot

Although zooming is not tracking, the same rules regarding pivoting apply. When the cameraman first uses a zoom lens he will probably find some difficulty in pivoting correctly. It is an unnatural action when it is not accompanied by camera movement, but practice should make him familiar with the technique needed. And he must remember to ensure that the panning head is correctly adjusted. This is particularly important when zooming is required.

Colour TV brought the extensive use of highly-mobile light-weight pedestals with 10:1 zoom lenses. Camera treatment changed accordingly. In achieving pace and flexibility, certain techniques developed, others regrettably lapsed.

The zoom lens made it all too easy to "pseudo-track" on static pedestals, instead of using true pedestal tracks. Rapid lens angle changes provided instantaneous close-ups. Adjustable lens angles permitted shot variety from isolated viewpoints (e.g. through

167

peepholes, from restricted positions). Lens angles could be adjusted to suit exactly the width of shot required. When there was not time to move a pedestal, a zoom-in nominally achieved the effect. Wide angles were often used for developing shots, the cameraman changing to a narrower angle as the shot tightened. A tendency grew to use a 35° lens for general purposes instead of a 24° lens. Shots became less precisely floor-marked, but instead were memorized for approximate positions. Such practices result in varying perspective and false drawing; not due to the zoom lens itself, but its usage.

Captions

Zooming in to captions at great speed can be very effective. But the captions must be designed for zooming if the operation is to be successful. Although it is not the cameraman's responsibility to ensure this, he is sometimes asked to advise on the suitability of certain captions for zooming. The following suggestions should help him establish the minimum size the captions should be in order to accommodate the full range of the zoom he is using.

Zoom in to the narrowest angle. Move the camera towards a caption-holder, until the limit of focus has been reached. At this point the camera cannot be moved closer to the board with the lens focused.

When this minimum distance has been reached, a card should be placed in the holder, and the limits of the area visible to the lens outlined in pencil. The lettering of the caption should be drawn within the area bounded by those lines.

The lens should then be zoomed out to its widest angle, and the limits of this wider area marked on the card. This is the minimum size that the caption-card should be. If it is cut to that size, and the lettering fitted into the smaller area previously marked, the cameraman will then be able to zoom into the caption from the widest to the narrowest angle of the zoom lens.

The zoom lens needs care in use, and speed of movement when resetting. And remember, if an artist has moved away from a position where he was formerly in focus, the focus correction will probably not be needed until the lens has been zoomed in. But then it is, of course, on its narrowest angle. There will be little depth of field, yet the cameraman must refocus as he is zooming.

The problem is analogous with an attempt to track with a narrow-angle lens, so far as technique is concerned. The cameraman must really concentrate in these circumstances.

The Crane

This piece of studio equipment was described in an earlier chapter. And the special technique needed to operate a camera mounted on a crane will be discussed later in the book.

But we cannot close the subject of camera movement without mentioning the forms of movement available with this highly versatile dolly. Also, since the trainee cameraman's first contact with the crane will be in the role of tracker, we can look at the requirements of that job.

When talking of the crane in this chapter we shall, for the sake of clarity, confine ourselves to the Mole Richardson type. This crane is one of the most widely used pieces of equipment of its kind in the British Isles, and the advice and comments regarding its operation can be easily adapted to similar dollies.

This equipment is capable of all the forms of camera movement which have already been described. It can also be "craned up" and "craned down", and it must be remembered that this type of movement is different in character from elevating and depressing the central column of a dolly. The crane arm can also be "jibbed right" or "jibbed left", which is not the same as crabbing.

When the central column of a pedestal is raised, the camera rises vertically. But if the arm of the crane is raised from its lowest to its highest point, the effect is rather different. For the first half of the movement—until the arm is in a horizontal position—the camera will move towards the subject. During the second half of the movement the camera will move away from the subject.

The same principle applies when the arm is jibbed—i.e. swung to the right or left about the central pivot. It is obvious that this is not the same form of movement as crabbing.

Simultaneous Movements

The versatility of the crane lies in its ability to provide a number of forms of camera movement simultaneously. And the exciting possibilities opened to the director and the cameraman by this equipment are endless.

The camera can rise high in the air, smoothly and quickly. It can be tracked in and craned down in one thrilling, swooping dive. It can rise diagonally; follow artists at great speed across the studio floor; look over the top of sets; peep through upstairs windows, and then drop like a bird to pick up an artist coming out through a door. The only limitations of the crane are its size, and the fact that it is rooted to the floor.

169

That is where the trackers enter the scene. They have to control this huge piece of equipment at the cameraman's bidding, and help provide the forms of unrestricted movement that the crane is capable of.

On the latest cranes one tracker is responsible for driving and steering, and he is usually referred to as the driver—though it is just as common to call him the tracker. The second man stands on the platform at the back of the crane, and swings the arm to provide the craning and jibbing motions. He is usually called the "swinger".

A good crew is worth its weight in gold. How true it is that a cameraman can never be any better than his trackers. Until they have mastered their jobs, and can provide the cameraman with smooth, precise movements with the minimum of signalling, the cameraman's opportunity to do justice to the equipment (and his own particular skill) will be restricted.

But once he has a trained, reliable crew tracking the crane—reacting instantly, almost instinctively, to the requirements of any situation—then the cameraman stands or falls according to his own ability.

It is a fact that a good crew can "carry" a bad cameraman. If they can see a studio monitor, they can almost frame his shots for him. They can take him through a transmission using the director's instructions only as their cues for movement. The harassed cameraman need only hang on to his panning handle, watch the headroom, and focus. He will find he has so much to do, that giving two men separate instructions while coping with the complexities of crane movement is impossible. He will love his trackers like brothers, and wonder why he left the safety of his pedestal dolly.

The cameraman is in the trackers' hands. They can make or break him. While it is true that an experienced cameraman can nurse an inexperienced crew through a show—in fact that is how they are trained—the sooner they learn their job the easier the cameraman and the director will breathe. Apart from the fact that a good tracker will be respected in his own right, his skill will stand him in good stead when he eventually graduates to actually operating the camera mounted on a crane.

It is a mistake to put an inexperienced tracker on a crane with an inexperienced cameraman. The effect can be a catastrophe for all concerned. Neither the cameraman nor the tracker learns his job. At best they might "get by": at worst the show can disintegrate.

Swinging the arm of the crane is a physically exhausting job, and it should not be given to small, weak men. Not only will it strain them, but they will be unable to carry out their tasks to the cameraman's satisfaction—and the programme will suffer.

The Driver

The driver has a responsible job, too. He must control the speed and direction of a piece of equipment weighing several tons. When moving from one set to another, he will often be called upon to drive and manoeuvre at speed, avoiding booms, other cameras, other sets, and people. The heavy crane can be difficult to stop once it is moving, but the driver must control it.

There have been cases of serious injury, and extensive damage to sets, when the crane has run amok. It is not the fault of the equipment. It is invariably due to the inexperience or carelessness of the tracker.

He should practise driving the crane as often as possible, until he is as familiar with it as he is with his own car. He will have to drive it so slowly during some tracks that it hardly seems to be moving. At other times he will frighten himself by the speed at which he will have to move. He might have to drive it through openings which are only inches wider than the crane—and he will have to do it first time, and every time, during the transmission of a programme.

He will probably find difficulty at first in controlling a piece of equipment fitted with rear-wheel steering. The technique is similar to reversing a car, but many an inexperienced tracker has taken the crane the "wrong way". It is an understandable mistake, and only constant practice will help the tracker to become proficient at this aspect of his work.

He must acquire confidence in himself. He must learn the scope and limitations of the equipment. And he must understand why the cameraman wants him to perform a particular manoeuvre, so that he can develop a feeling for the speed of any track.

The Swinger

The swinger, too, must acquire a feeling for the nature of his duties. He must devise a method of marking his "crib-card" (which is described in a later chapter) so that the camera is always at the agreed height for every shot. And all movements of the crane arm should be in sympathy with the director's and the cameraman's intentions.

Cameraman's Signals

So the tracker, whether he is driving or swinging, must concentrate. He must watch the cameraman's signalling-hand as if his job depends on it—as it probably does. His hands must be on the controls—or on the bucket at the back of the crane arm—and he must respond *immediately* to the cameraman's signals. When the cameraman is satisfied with a particular position for a shot, or a line for a track, or the height of movement of the crane arm, the tracker must mark his card accordingly.

In the case of the driver, he must also mark the position of the dolly on the studio floor. He can please himself which part of the crane he aligns to these marks. Some trackers use the rear wheel-hub as a reference point, and make all marks on the studio floor in line with that. Others use the screw holding the side cable-guards as a guide. It does not matter what he chooses, as long as it is easily visible, and he sticks to it.

If he is in doubt about the speed of a particular track or swing, or about the exact position of the crane for a certain shot, he should mention it to the cameraman. It is important that he has these things clear in his own mind. If he can delay taxing the cameraman with these questions until after rehearsals, so much the better. But he must never go on the air with doubts in his mind.

If the tracker has kept alert during rehearsals, marking the "crib-card" and the floor diligently, he should be capable of going through the show with a minimum of signals from the cameraman. A nod to indicate the beginning and end of a track or swing is all that should be necessary. The cameraman has an exceptionally difficult job to do. Anything the tracker can do to reduce the need for signalling will be appreciated.

The cameraman will sometimes have to twist his body into unnatural positions for the start or finish of a movement. It will be difficult for him to give signals to two people, and keep control of his camera at the same time. In these circumstances the tracker should be satisfied with a nod from the cameraman; and the nod should indicate that a movement previously rehearsed should now be performed. No further instructions should be necessary.

The tracker should make a note, if only in his own mind, of the lens the cameraman is using for each shot. He will then be more aware of the problems of the cameraman, and he will know (from his own experience with a camera) how close he should take the dolly in order to get a particular shot on a particular lens.

When the cameraman is using a narrow-angle lens, or when he is framing a delicate shot, the tracker must keep any movement he must make on the dolly down to a minimum. He is there to serve the cameraman. He is there to respond to his slightest wish, and he must do nothing which might interfere with the cameraman's task.

If a cameraman signals a tracker to stop tracking, and the director orders the track to continue, what is the tracker to do? Well! Whenever the cameraman's signals do not agree with the director's instructions, the tracker must *always* obey the cameraman.

There may be many reasons why the cameraman has ignored the director. There may be reasons (which neither the director nor the tracker are aware of) why he *cannot* follow out instructions. It is the cameraman's responsibility to decide what to do in the circumstances; the tracker need not get involved. Even if the show is ruined by this defiance of the director's instructions, the tracker will not be blamed if he has carried out the cameraman's orders. But woe betide the tracker who ignores the cameraman!

The tracker must remember his duties, even during the later, tiring hours of a long rehearsal. There may be times when he feels that he is forgotten and unimportant. But this is not the case. He must concentrate on the job, watch the cameraman for the most imperceptible of signals, and do all he can to relieve him of the extra responsibilities that operating a crane-mounted camera entails.

Apart from the fact that he will be doing an important job well, he must remember that one day he will sit at the front. Then he will expect the same assistance from *his* trackers.

If there are opportunities for crew-training sessions at his studio, the tracker should ask to be allowed to "sit at the front" of the crane, and then he should endeavour to operate the camera and control his trackers simultaneously. This is the best introduction to the requirements of tracking he can experience. He will almost certainly be amazed at the difficulties the cameraman faces, and he will understand—vividly and permanently—how he as a tracker can help overcome them. The tracker must mentally tune himself to the needs of the cameraman.

For this reason the best trackers are cameramen; and the best cameramen are invariably those who mastered the technique of tracking early in their career.

13

REHEARSALS AND TRANSMISSIONS

A GOOD cameraman can play a major part in avoiding wasted rehearsal time. He will line up his shots quickly, with a minimum of instructions from the director. He will interpret the director's intentions from the details on his "crib-card", and present the right shots at the right time.

When he has finished shooting a series of shots in a particular set, he will move to the next set, and be ready to carry on there as soon as the director is ready. The director will have to explain his intentions for many of the shots, but the cameraman can, by intelligent application of his knowledge and technique, keep such instructions to the minimum.

Before rehearsals, the director will have had detailed technical and operational planning meetings with the senior members of the production team (the technical and lighting directors, designer, make-up, costume, etc.); followed, for large shows, by outside (non-studio) rehearsals. As a result, by the time the show enters the studio, all major stumbling blocks should have been overcome. The cameraman should be free to execute the concepts of the realization team. His basic positions have been marked for him on the studio camera plan, types of shots planned, types of mountings and his cable-routings arranged.

Preparing to Shoot

Cameramen must always be ready to commence rehearsals at the scheduled time, with their equipment correctly set up. Most studios allow a period of half an hour or so to enable technical crews to assemble and prepare their equipment for the particular show in hand.

They must be punctual then. Any cameraman who has kept an impatient director waiting for five minutes, will know how long they can seem. In fact, delaying rehearsals is inconsiderate, since so many other people must wait until the cameraman is ready.

By the time that rehearsals are due to start, cameramen must have attended to all the tasks that fall within their responsibility. Lenses must be mounted in the correct order on the turret, and set at the required f stop: the right camera must be on the right dolly: the camera cables must be attached to their respective connections around the wall of the studio, bearing in mind the complicated intermingling of equipment which will take place during the show: each camera must be placed on its first position for the programme, with the cameraman and trackers standing-by.

The director is entitled to be irritated if details such as these are not attended to.

Prior to the actual transmission of a programme the cameraman must double-check his equipment. Are the lens apertures set at the required stop? Is the camera dolly in position for the first shot and pointing in the right direction? Are the "crib-cards" in the correct order? Are the marks he made on the floor still visible?

He must check everything, leaving nothing to chance. Many cameramen devise a set routine of pre-transmission checks, and this ensures that nothing is ever overlooked. It is a good idea, and all cameramen should invent a similar routine which suits them personally.

Since a mistake at the beginning of a transmission can sometimes unsettle a cameraman for the rest of the programme, many of them memorize the first half-dozen shots they must take. This works very well for some individuals, and if a cameraman is particularly nervous, he might experiment with the method—it could help him over the first, terrifying minute.

The Shooting Script

Let us assume that a television play is about to be performed. This type of television programme usually utilizes to the full the technique of each section of the studio, and other programmes can be more easily compared in relation to it.

Three or four cameras are normally used on a show of this nature. Occasionally, when facilities exist, as many as six cameras are employed, but this practice is comparatively rare.

The "master-plan" for the show is the director's script, which contains the full dialogue and actions of the actors, as for a stage play. Let us say that the director in this example is using three cameras, each equipped with four lenses, and mounted on movable pedestals or trackable dollies. This means that he has at his dis-

175

posal an infinite variety of pictures with which to present the play to the viewers.

The director must visualize the play as a series of pictures. He must then decide when he will change one picture for another, which cameras he will use, how the transition from one to the other will be made and so on. We need not concern ourselves with these problems of the director's job at this stage. A knowledge of them is necessary only to understand the following.

As we know, each picture is called a shot, and each shot will be numbered chronologically as it is decided upon. The point in the play where each shot will be taken will be marked on the script by the director. A description of the shot, and the number of the camera taking it will also be recorded.

THE SHOOTING SCRIPT

Cameras	Action	Sound
	Interior FREDDY'S room (Evening).	
30 CUT CAM. I. Pos. "D" M.S. Freddy. Pan him from door to bunk.	(FREDDY bursts through door, crosses to bunk (right) and throws himself face-down on to it.)	BOOM "A".
31 CUT CAM. 2. Pos. "B". M.C.U. Sue.	(SUE enters.) SUE: Congratulations! You were wonderful. You should have seen their faces.	
32 CUT CAM. I. M.C.U. Freddy.	(FREDDY lifts his head and stares at her.) FREDDY: Go on—laugh if you think it's funny.	
33 CUT CAM. 2. M.S. Sue Pan right as she crosses to chair M2S. incl. Freddy.	(SUE laughs, crosses to chair near bunk and sits.) SUE: I am. I do. And that sister of yours. . . . (She mimics AGNES in the way she sits, then doubles up with laughter.)	
34 CUT CAM. I. C.U. Freddy. CAM. 2. Clear to pos. "C" garden set.	FREDDY: Well I gotta live with them and I don't think it's funny. A nice little mess you got me into. Now see if you can get me out of it.	
35 CUT CAM. 3. Pos. "E" O/S2S. fav. Sue As she kneels T.I. to tight 2S. fav. Sue.	(SUE rises, crosses to FREDDY and kneels close to him.) SUE: But that's why I'm here, dear boy— to do just that. I'm going to get you out of it.	
36 CUT CAM. I Pos. "E". Tight 2S. fav. Freddy.	FREDDIE: Out of what? What are you on about?	

176

37	CUT		
	CAM. 3. Tight 2S. as before.	SUE: I'm on about the place beyond the perimeters of this petty battlefield.	SOUNDS OF GLASS BREAK-ING AND ANGRY SHOUTS FROM KITCHEN.
38	CUT		BOOM "B".
	CAM. I. Pos. "D" M2S.	FREDDY (a little awed): You. . . . You mean that place you told me about? SUE: Where a legion of free-thinking men are congregating in strength.	
	Pan with Freddy to M.S. at window.	FREDDY: How? (He rises suddenly and crosses to window. Opens it and looks out. After a second or two he turns to face SUE.) What have I got to do? Tell me what I've got to do and I'll do anything you say. Just let me know and I'll do it.	Q GRAMS STREET NOISES.
39	CUT		
	CAM. 3. M.S. Sue. She rises.	(SUE rises.) SUE: It isn't as easy as that. FREDDY: Well, there's bound to be some way. What is it then?	Q GRAMS CROSS FADE FROM STREET
	T.I. to M.C.U.	SUE: Think. Think. Think, dear boy. Reason for yourself. If you don't use your reason you're lost. Take a look at them in there. . . .	NOISES TO MOOD MUSIC.

The script will also contain information on the variety of sound that the director wants, cues to artists, lighting effects and changes, details of film inserts, etc. In fact, the script will contain a wealth of information, all of which is important to the director. He is the controlling factor, the man who "wields the baton", as it were.

The cameraman does not need all this information. It is sufficient for him to know only the relevant details of each shot he will have to take with the camera he is operating.

The Crib Card

Each cameraman will normally be handed his own series of cards—"crib cards" (camera cards)—that are clipped beside the camera viewfinder. These list each shot in order for that camera, with its scripted shot number, showing composition details, actor and mounting moves, etc. As much information as possible about every shot will be included, together with the position which the camera must occupy on the floor during the course of the production.

These camera positions, usually lettered A-Z, correspond with camera positions marked on a floor-plan, which will have been prepared by the director. The crib-card will also contain any special instructions to the cameraman, such as fast moves from one set to another, or special mirror shots.

177

The following example of part of a crib-card for Camera One illustrates the above.

CRIB CARD

			Camera One	Card Seven
Shot No.	Pos.	Lens	Description	Area
30	D		MS Freddy PAN HIM FROM DOOR TO BUNK	INT. FREDDY'S ROOM
32			MCU FREDDY	
34			CU FREDDY	
36	E		TIGHT 2S FAV. FREDDY	
38	D		M2S PAN FREDDY TO MS AT WINDOW	

It will be seen that space has been left on the card to enable the cameraman to record the lens he will use for each shot. There are three common methods of indicating this on the crib-card.

In the first method the cameraman records the focal length of the lens he is using (2 in., 5 in., 8 in., etc.). In the second, the angle of view of each lens is noted (9 degrees, 25 degrees, etc.).

The third method involves writing the turret position on the card (see page 72). Many cameramen claim that this method is quicker and safer than the first two. They maintain that if they are taking a shot on position two on the turret, for example, and they see that according to the marked crib-card the next shot has to be taken on turret position four, there will be no mental effort or calculation necessary before they swing the turret to the next lens.

If, however, they had recorded the lenses only in each case—3 in. and 8 in.—these figures would have to be converted into turret-position numbers before swinging to the new position. It may take only a split second, and can become automatic, but there are dangers.

If the normal range of lenses on the turret is varied—2 in., 3 in., 5 in., and 8 in. lenses being replaced by 3 in., 5 in., 8 in., and 12 in. lenses respectively—the cameraman will have to re-learn the turret position which corresponds with each lens. On fast sequences he might fall back on habit, and swing to position two (where the 3 in. lens is normally located), only to find that he has located the 5 in. lens.

This cannot happen if he records the turret positions only for each shot, and this is why many cameramen favour this method. It is up to the individual, however. For zoom lenses one may use the numbered "shot box", note the metered lens angles, or, quite often, simply remember the "feel" of each shot.

Marking the Studio Floor

When each shot has been framed to the director's satisfaction, and the lens or turret position marked on the crib-card, the cameraman should mark the position of his dolly on the studio floor. Then he will know that whenever he places his dolly on that spot during transmission, and locates the lens he has marked on his card, his shot will be the one which was agreed in rehearsal.

Once again, cameramen settle on their own particular methods of marking the position of the dolly. There are dozens of variations on this theme. A simple method is to draw a line along that part of the dolly which is nearest the cameraman's feet, draw a second line at right-angles to the first to indicate the centre of the dolly, and give the position a letter. The first position will be "A", the second "B", and so on.

These letters must also be recorded on the crib-card, and the cameraman can then place himself in the correct position for any shot, at any time, with a minimum of delay. The cameraman must get into the habit of marking his crib-card and the studio floor for each of his shots. Eventually, experience will allow him to dispense with many of these marks, but the trainee cameraman must acquire the habit, and stick to it.

Most directors mark all the estimated positions each camera will occupy on a floor-plan. Before rehearsals commence, the cameraman should study this floor-plan and note where he is expected to place his camera for each shot. Since many directors are capable of forecasting these positions to an accuracy of within three inches, cameramen must always start at these planned marks, deviating from them only if the shot is not to the director's satisfaction. They must not wander around the studio at will, placing their cameras where *they* think they should be.

We have already mentioned the fact that cameramen must take care when matching shots with each other. The framing of one medium close-up must be identical with medium close-ups on other cameras. All matching cameras must be at the same height, and that the shots should be taken on similar lenses.

By attending to these details himself the cameraman can avoid wasted rehearsal time. Such details as marking the crib-card, matching shots and so on, are part of the cameraman's job, and he should attend to them without waiting for the director's instructions. Cameramen should study other cameramen's shots on the studio monitor, and make any final adjustments of framing themselves to improve matching, continuity and composition.

Fast Moves and Lens Changes

Cameramen are often called upon to change to the next shot in an extremely short space of time. Let us say that shot No. 32 on Camera One is a long shot of a set, and that the next shot on this camera will be No. 34, which is a close-up of an artist. The cameraman must change his shot when the director has cut to shot No. 33, on Camera Two, say. But shot No. 33 may be held for four seconds only. In the space of four seconds the cameraman operating Camera One must change to a tighter lens, possibly move his dolly closer to the artist, reframe his shot, refocus, and allow the vision control operator time to make his electronic adjustments.

The cameraman should perform all these operations with time to spare. As a golden rule—and this applies whatever the time at his disposal—he must always be quite certain in advance what his next shot is going to be. He must never wait until the director has cut away from him before trying to find his place on the crib-card. He must find time, while taking one shot, to glance at his card and make a mental note of the next shot.

In particular, he must note if a lens change is needed, and determine the direction in which he must swing the turret in order to locate the new lens. As soon as the light on his camera goes out (indicating that the cut to Camera Two has been made) he should swing the turret to the new position. If he has to move the dolly at the same time, he should push it in with his foot *as* he is changing lenses. There is no time for delay. He must know what he is going to do as soon as the director cuts away from his camera, and do it immediately the cut has been made.

Remember that if the cameraman has to change his shot from a long shot of an artist to a close-up, he will have to refocus forward once the tighter lens has been located. He can save time by focusing forward as soon as the lens change has been accomplished. He should never have to hunt for focus by moving the focusing mechanism backwards and forwards.

With practice, the cameraman will find that he can change to

180

another lens, reframe the shot, and refocus, in less than a second. A lot depends, of course, on the focusing mechanism of the particular camera he is operating. But an amazing speed can be reached by the cameraman with practice.

If he has to move his camera quickly from one set to another, and also change lenses, he should always change to a new lens *before* he reaches the new set. Provided he has time, he can change lenses before he leaves the set on which he has been working. Where this would waste too much time, he must swing the turret to the new position *as* he is moving the dolly. In any case he must make every effort to change lenses away from live microphones.

There is a good reason for changing to the new lens before reaching the next set. If the move is a very fast one, or if it is delayed for any reason, there is a danger that the cameraman—in his hurry to frame the new shot—will forget that he has to change lenses. He might reach the new set and hurriedly frame and focus his shot before being aware of the mistake.

In the meantime, the director might have been waiting for the cameraman to reach the set and offer the next shot. He will be tempted to cut to the camera as soon as he sees a framed and focused picture. This cut usually coincides with the cameraman's realization that he is on the wrong lens, and we get the disturbing sight of a lens change in vision.

This is not, by any means, an uncommon occurrence. It can always be avoided, however, if all lens changes are completed immediately the director cuts to another camera. The cameraman must ensure, therefore, that he knows all the necessary details of his next shot *before* the director cuts away.

We have mentioned the problems of the vision control operator in an earlier chapter. The cameraman depends on him for properly exposed, well-defined pictures, among other things. But the cameraman can make his life easier if he remembers his own obligations.

The cameraman should settle on each new shot as soon as possible, and then hold it until the vision control operator has completed his electronic adjustments. These adjustments will be necessary for all substantial changes of picture framing. The new shot must also be matched to the shots from other cameras, and all this takes time. The sooner the vision control operator sees each shot, the happier will he be.

Cameramen must resist the temptation, during rehearsals, to take shots "just for the fun of it". The operator at the camera control unit will assume that each shot is necessary, and adjust his controls. He will not be amused, after a few hours of this, to learn that the cameraman was "only looking around".

If there are any particularly fast changes of shots to be made, the cameraman should warn his operator of this during rehearsals. If necessary, he should perform the fast change a few times so that the vision control operator can practise his adjustments.

When Things Go Wrong

Television is a complicated business. Apart from the thousands of electronic and mechanical components that go to make up a smooth-running production, a great many people are involved. They must all be expected to carry out the tasks they are entrusted with, and they must perform these tasks at a set time in co-operation with others.

When the programme is "on the air" there must be no mistakes. The mistake of one man in one section can so affect the work of other sections, that the show can snowball into a disaster for all concerned.

But people are human; and human beings make mistakes. The components of a television camera will not last for ever, and are not at all shy of breaking down during a high-budget spectacular.

A door will not open; an artist forgets his lines; a camera cable finds its way underneath the camera-guards, and the cameraman's move is delayed; a stage-hand accidentally knocks a set-brace, and the set collapses; a camera breaks down; a microphone fails; we could go on for hours. Such things happen, despite care. Some are common occurrences, but all are potentially ruinous so far as any television production is concerned. Fortunately, videotape recording usually allows corrective retakes.

What is the cameraman to do when things go wrong? This can best be answered by dividing these accidents into two categories. Those that do not concern him, and those that do. This may seem very obvious, but the division is important.

In the first place, most of the things that go wrong during a programme should not concern the cameraman. Artists' "fluffs" and microphone failures, for example, are not his concern. More than that, they must not be allowed to distract him from his own job. Competent camerawork depends on concentration, and a lapse of a couple of seconds can destroy this, with potentially disastrous results.

182

The cameraman must remember that if something has gone seriously wrong in another department, the accident will affect the show least if he concentrates all the harder on his own tasks. He must force himself to remain completely oblivious of falling china, an artist with his shirt hanging out, or an orchestra and singer who sound as if they are on separate pages of the music.

They are not his concern: they must be dismissed from his mind. There are other people who will deal with them, who are, in fact, responsible for doing just that. And in the event of a really calamitous accident, it is the director who must take the helm and do what he can to rescue the sinking show.

The cameraman's worries are normally centred around either the failure of part of his equipment, or his inability to offer a shot when it is expected.

A typical example of a technical failure is a viewfinder fault. The picture may become distorted, or crushed. Severe flashing and tearing of the picture might be serious enough to interfere with the cameraman's work. In extreme cases the viewfinder might cease to function altogether, leaving the cameraman with no means of knowing what he is framing.

Except in the case of total failure of the viewfinder, it is usually possible for the cameraman to continue to frame his shots throughout the show in such a way that only experienced technicians would realize that something was wrong. He should certainly do his best to carry on, though if he has talk-back facilities he should inform the director of his predicament. Any slight irregularities in framing, or focus, can usually be corrected by a competent director, who will almost certainly manage to nurse the "sick" camera through the rest of the programme.

Naturally, if the viewfinder has failed altogether the cameraman is helpless. He must inform the director immediately, and also get word to the maintenance engineers, who should be in a position to replace his viewfinder with a "working spare" within minutes.

In the meantime, the other cameramen engaged on the show must be prepared to take over some of the shots of the camera that is out of commission. But they must remember that the director is the man in charge. They must be guided by him.

An experienced cameraman can often save a show in these circumstances. He will vary his shots to compensate for the loss of another camera, without waiting for the director's instructions. His instinct and training, together with his knowledge of the actual conditions on the studio floor, make him the ideal man to contend with this emergency. But unless a cameraman has many years of experience, and dozens of similar situations behind him, he must follow the director's instructions.

A viewfinder fault has been given as a typical example. But the same procedure applies to other technical faults that can occur on a camera. If the cameraman can possibly manage to continue, he must do so. During transmission the director can be a very harassed man, and the cameraman must not add to his problems.

It is not uncommon for a cameraman to be delayed during a move to another part of the studio, or even failing to complete the move altogether. A thoughtless artist might block his path, his camera cable might become entangled with other pieces of equipment, in his haste he might run into pieces of scenery: the studio floor can be a very crowded place.

Whatever the circumstances, he must not force the director to by-pass a shot. There is a reason for every shot. The director will have planned and rehearsed his programme around the camera shots, and he is entitled to expect the cameraman to present him with each rehearsed shot during transmission.

Further, cutting to a new shot very often provides an opportunity for the cameraman who had taken the previous shot to swing to another lens, or change his camera position. If the new shot is not there, these cannot be attempted, and a chain reaction of errors will be set in motion.

If a cameraman cannot place his camera in the right position in time for his next shot (or within a second or two at the most) he must do his best to offer a shot as similar as possible to the one that had been rehearsed.

If, for example, he cannot approach close enough to frame an artist in mid-shot with a normal-angle lens, he must try to frame a similar shot using a narrower angle lens.

Even if this shot bears little resemblance to the original, it is infinitely superior to none at all. As soon as the director has cut to another camera, the cameraman must move his camera into the correct position in the set where he can continue framing his shots as rehearsed.

Working with Others

The cameraman is not the most important man on the studio floor. He is part of a team, and he must remember that. It is safe to say that everyone on the studio floor is important; if they were not, they would not be there. This point has been made before, but it can never be overstated.

In order to become a useful member of the team, the cameraman must first become skilled at his own job—that is obvious. But he must also remember that his camerawork is often limited by the work of the members of other sections. They, too, would like conditions in the studio to be arranged to suit themselves. But, of course, this just is not possible.

The set designer, for example, is impeded by cost restriction, by space and mechanics, by limitations of colour. The lighting director would like to light each shot individually. But he must arrange his lighting to cover continuous movement, and a variety of camera positions. And he is continually harassed by the need to throw the shadow of the boom microphone on to some part of the set which will not be seen in any shot.

The boom operator, for his part, cannot always place his microphone in the ideal position to cover the sound from any subject. He must, at all costs, prevent the microphone from being seen in a cameraman's shot. And he must play his part in preventing the shadow from his microphone from being seen.

When the director cuts to a close-up of an artist, the boom operator can place his microphone very close to the artist's face. But the next shot might be a wide shot, or a group shot, and he will have to raise his microphone before that shot is taken.

On a programme containing a hundred or more shots he can be a very busy man. The skilled boom operator will memorize the occasions when it is safe for him to place his microphone close to an artist, and also the times when he must hurriedly raise it to clear the next shot. His job is not made any easier by the cameraman whose shots on transmission differ from those which have been rehearsed.

As we know, the cameraman must work in close co-operation with the boom operator. A certain amount of give and take is needed on both sides, and this cannot be attained unless they each understand the other's problems. The cameraman must pay particular attention to the headroom he allows for every shot, and the chapter on picture framing should help him along these lines. Above all, he must be consistent, and the shots he takes during transmission must be the same as those which were finalized during the last rehearsal.

The cameraman must also acquire a working knowledge of television lighting. A lighting director cannot possibly light a subject or a set so that it can be shot from every conceivable angle. The cameraman must shoot his subjects within the limitations laid down by the lighting director. The director might be delighted by a shot from an unexpected angle offered by an enthusiastic cameraman. But unless this shot is taken within the lighting director's limits, the cameraman will almost certainly incur his wrath.

In fact, co-operation with other sections is simply a matter of knowing one's own job, understanding the problems of others, and adding a large measure of common sense.

The problem of dealing with artists has already been discussed in the chapter on the television cameraman. The cameraman is reminded that artists are merely human beings—albeit exceptional human beings in many cases—and they should be treated with respect, but without awe.

But the person who needs the cameraman's co-operation most is, without doubt, the director. The cameraman who is incompetent and unco-operative can be a worry to the director. Rehearsal time can be criminally wasted by a cameraman who takes three or four times as long as another cameraman to line up his shots.

But, further than that, the cameraman's approach to each shot should be in sympathy with the director's intentions. This is where a basic sense of artistry is necessary in the make-up of any good television cameraman.

It may take the director ten minutes to explain to a cameraman who has little artistic feeling exactly what he had in mind when he planned the shot. But the good cameraman would have grasped this from the details on his crib-card, and from the mood of the action-taking place in front of him.

His first duty is to be a competent cameraman, however. No programme, however brilliantly planned, can possibly succeed if the cameramen are incapable of framing well-composed shots, or executing smooth, unobtrusive camera movement, to name only two basic techniques.

Interpreting the Mood

Mere competence is not enough. No programme can rise above the mediocre without the co-operation of cameramen who interpret the mood the director wishes to create. Although it is very dangerous for the cameraman to allow himself to become too involved in the subject matter of a programme, he must capture this sense of mood.

This is particularly vital in the case of musical programmes. As

186

we discussed earlier, the speed of camera movement should be governed by the tempo and mood of the music. A cameraman who is not mentally "tuned" to the music cannot possibly hope to inject any feeling into his work.

Although a musical show is the best example, the need is still there on other types of programmes. If the cameraman is not naturally sensitive or artistic, he can still acquire this feeling for mood. He can do this by considering carefully the reason behind every shot which he is required to take.

Why did the director put it on his script? What was the previous shot and what will be the next? Why has he asked for a track on this shot, and why has he asked that another shot be taken from a low angle?

These are the sort of questions the cameraman should ask himself when he is studying his crib-card and lining up his shots during rehearsal. In time he can inject feeling into his shots. But until then he should ask himself similar questions to these, and if he cannot work out the answers for himself he should ask the director.

Learning to Relax

One of the most common faults of inexperienced cameramen is their inability to operate a camera during transmission as competently as they had done during rehearsals. This is, of course, simply a matter of stage-fright. Every transmission is equivalent to a first night in a theatre.

The cameraman might well be nervous, as he should be if he has any feeling in him. He will probably be tense, physically and mentally, and inclined to try that little bit too hard. Before attempting a difficult track he will tend to grip the panning handle a little tighter, check focus for the twentieth time, and grit his teeth. But, as we discussed in an earlier chapter, he *should* be relaxed.

But this is just what he is not. It is small consolation for him to know that relaxation will come with experience. He is "on the air" *now*: the director has cued him to start his track. He is entirely on his own, and no one can help him. There is certainly no opportunity for him to rehearse his shot just once more.

He must *force* himself to relax. If he finds that he is gripping the panning handle too tightly, he should slacken his grip. If his body is tense, his camerawork will suffer. During rehearsals he was probably relaxed. If he made a mistake, or if a camera movement was not properly executed, it did not matter very much. There

187

would be further opportunities to practise and perfect each shot, and he was under no particular tension.

But transmissions are a different kettle of fish. Everything must be perfect, and the thought is terrifying.

It is true that this feeling will disappear with experience, although transmissions will always demand more from him than rehearsals. If he has all the qualities of a good cameraman, he will—or should —feel some nervous excitement before he goes "on the air" to transmit a major programme. But once the show has started he will give of his best.

The trainee cameraman can overcome his nervousness best if he makes a concentrated effort to keep his mind alert and his body relaxed. If he has been able to perform certain camera movements—or execute some difficult shots—during rehearsals, he should remind himself constantly that he can do it again. He must have confidence in himself.

He can acquire this by practising his shots over and over again during rehearsals until they are perfect. The need to practise his technique continually has been emphasized throughout this book, but it is so essential that it is mentioned again. Practice leads to skill, and skill breeds confidence. There is nothing like confidence in himself to overcome the cameraman's apprehensions.

With experience and practice, we become more able to *anticipate*. Although for instance we find ourselves with plenty of time to make camera moves or lens-changes during early slow-paced stopping-rehearsals, we do not forget that for the final run-through and the recording (or transmission) the pace will often have hotted up. These same moves then have to be made smartly, during the normal speed of continuous production. This does not perturb the experienced cameraman, but he takes care to check that any fast changes during early rehearsal will still be feasible in the final production run.

One-Man Show

Some nervous people are consoled by the thought that others have endured more harassing situations than they themselves are facing. It might be worth mentioning, then, one of the most difficult and exciting tasks a cameraman can be called upon to perform.

Some directors have planned and shot a full-length programme using one camera only. If such a show is carefully planned and rehearsed, there is no doubt that this technique can add an exciting originality to the programme.

188

But the cameraman takes the major strain of such a venture. His technique must be excellent, and his nerves strong. He must never lose focus at any time—there will be no cuts to other cameras when he can surreptitiously check and correct this. He cannot— must not—relax his concentration.

Since one movement must flow into the next, he must always anticipate the positions his body must take in order to perform these continuous movements.

In fact, this type of show is an exciting, terrifying challenge, which few cameramen could resist. But the nervous strain is considerable, as any cameraman who has endured this type of programme will confirm.

Learning from Mistakes

Many cameramen adopt the technique known to actors and speakers of breathing slowly and deeply before commencing their "ordeal". This helps to steady the nerves and relax the body. Nervous cameramen might experiment with this suggestion if they are having difficulty in controlling the tension they feel before a transmission.

Finally, it must be made clear that the cameraman must never brood over any mistakes he might make. This is fatal, since it can affect his camerawork for the rest of the programme.

If he does commit an error his first duty is to rectify it as soon as possible. Having done so he *must* then dismiss it from his mind. No good can come from personally castigating himself—in fact, the reverse is the case.

All cameramen make mistakes—especially during their "early days"—and the trainee will almost certainly commit a number of blunders. The time to review them is *after* the programme has been transmitted. Then he should study the reasons which led to his mistakes, and determine never to allow them to happen again.

14

LATER TECHNIQUES

As the standard of the cameraman's technique improves, so will he become entrusted with more involved camerawork. This progression from the least important to the most important camera on a programme will normally take a steady, logical form. The cameraman might be unaware of the progress he is making in his profession until he looks back at his early days. This is probably true of all walks of life.

But situations might occur without warning when a cameraman will be expected to skip two or three rungs of the ladder he is climbing. A more experienced cameraman might be taken ill, or holiday commitments might have reduced the strength of the crew, for example. Every cameraman should be prepared for such an eventuality.

It is hoped that this chapter will provide some guidance to the cameraman whose basic technique is sound, but who lacks experience of more involved camerawork.

Camera Dolly

Operating a camera which is mounted on a camera dolly for the first time can be a rather unnerving experience. No longer is the cameraman able to dictate the movement of his dolly at will, as he could when operating a camera mounted on a pedestal. Then, he had only to think of a movement and his body would react. The versatility of his dolly depended only on the extent of his own manual co-ordination coupled with the speed of his reflexes.

Sitting on the front of a camera dolly, with a tracker to control, is a different matter altogether. The dolly will not move merely because the cameraman wants it to. He must first let the tracker know that he wants to move. He must also let him know the speed at which he wants the track to be performed, and the direction which it should take. He must also tell the tracker when to stop.

This cannot be done by word of mouth during a transmission. Instead, the cameraman must rely on a system of signals to his trackers. And this is what is so confusing to the inexperienced. For in addition to the normal problems of correct framing, focusing, and keeping the camera steady, he has the added responsibility of controlling the trackers.

Something has to suffer—his camerawork or his control over the trackers. Unfortunately, the harassed cameraman will usually find that, in fact, both suffer badly at first.

Most cameramen who are unaccustomed to being tracked, seem to find it impossible to concentrate on their camerawork and give clear concise signals to their trackers at the same time. This is understandable, and it is a technique which comes with experience.

Devising a Signal System

Unfortunately there is no standard set of signals which the cameraman can learn to help him through this phase. Each cameraman has his own method of signalling—it is usually a natural reaction on his part. But however the signals may vary from one cameraman to another, they all have the same qualities— they are concise and unambiguous.

If the tracker is experienced—as he should be if an inexperienced cameraman is operating the camera—he will respond to the gentlest of signals from the cameraman. But he must first understand the meaning of each movement of the cameraman's fingers or hand.

If the cameraman has operated as a tracker during part of his training, he should have become accustomed to the types of signals used by more experienced cameramen. When he is being tracked himself, he should try to imitate those signals for the benefit of his own tracker. He must remember the difficulties of tracking, and the need for clear, concise signals.

If he signals that he wants the dolly to track in, and it moves backwards, he should not belabour the poor tracker. He should first of all check that he had given the signal he intended to give. He must not expect the tracker to make do with vague flutterings of his hand.

The cameraman relies on the tracker for successful camera movement. And successful movement depends on correct signalling. A cameraman should not begrudge any time spent in establishing a foolproof system of control over his trackers.

Most cameramen make the basic mistake of failing to signal

the end of a track. The beginning is easy enough. The director cues the start of a movement, the cameraman signals, and the dolly moves happily forward.

But the cameraman can become so involved in the problems of framing, focusing, and keeping the camera steady, that he can easily forget to signal the tracker to stop the track. He might decide to end the track at a certain point, and then forget entirely that he must signal the tracker to do just that. It is amazing how often this happens, and many an artist has fled from the path of a dolly containing a forgetful cameraman and an obedient tracker.

This is something that the cameraman must guard against from the beginning. It is far better to prepare for this particular eventuality than to learn by bitter experience.

There is another basic error which invariably reveals the inexperience of the cameraman, and it shows itself particularly on the type of dolly which provides the tracker with the power to vary the height of the camera. Unless he is very careful, the cameraman is liable to allow his camera to dip slightly at the beginning and end of any changes of camera height.

An equally common fault is for the inexperienced cameraman either to fail to pivot about the top of the frame immediately the height is varied, or to pivot a fraction of a second before the movement has started.

He will learn, in time, the delay he can expect between the giving of a signal and the response of the tracker. This will come with experience. No tracker can respond instantly to instructions, and the cameraman must learn to give his signals in advance— just before he expects the movement to start or stop. The amount of time to be allowed will vary from one tracker to another. But it is a good idea to try to make every tracker respond as quickly as the best. This helps improve the standard of tracking on the crew.

Each type of camera dolly has its own peculiarities, and some are particularly unsuitable for the first attempts of the inexperienced cameraman. Operating a camera mounted on a Mole Richardson Motion Picture Crane, for example, is a highly skilled job. Cameramen should try to obtain some experience on other types of dollies before attempting work of this nature.

Manually-Tracked Dolly

The simplest camera dolly is the type which is pushed by the tracker. Raising and lowering the arm which supports the camera and cameraman is normally achieved by means of a wheel, operated by the tracker. All movements on this dolly will be relatively slow and smooth, and the cameraman will have time to adjust himself to his new environment. This type of dolly provides the ideal vehicle for the transition from pedestal to electrically-driven dolly.

Many of the manually-tracked dollies can be jibbed (or-tongued) to right or left. For mechanical reasons this operation must invariably be performed slowly, and this helps the cameraman to acclimatize himself to the technique of this rather strange movement.

He must remember, though, that jibbing is not the same as crabbing. When crabbing, the camera normally travels parallel to a scene. Jibbing, however, moves the camera in an arc, the radius of which is the length of the arm of the dolly.

If the camera is jibbed from the extreme left-hand position to the extreme right-hand position, the camera will move closer to the scene as it nears the head-on position. Once past this, it will then move progressively away from the scene until it reaches the extreme right-hand position.

Depending on the lens being used, the nearness of the subject, and the stop at which the lens is set, some focus correction might be necessary during this manoeuvre. The cameraman must pay careful attention to the need to pivot during the jibbing movement. He must start pivoting as soon as the movement commences—not before or after—and stop as soon as the movement ceases.

Motorized Dolly

The electrically-driven dolly is the next logical step forward for the cameraman. Here the tracker normally stands at the back of the dolly and controls its movement with the help of an electric motor. He can set the dolly in motion almost instantaneously, govern its speed, and stop it just as quickly with the brake. The dolly can be driven both in a forward and reverse direction, and the tracker steers by means of a steering wheel acting on the two rear wheels of the dolly, so all-round vision is essential always.

On some early types of motorized dollies the tracker was also responsible for raising or lowering the arm carrying the camera and cameraman. But on later models this control was given to the cameraman—to the relief of all trackers. Driving and steering is a full-time job, and it really was asking a little too much of any tracker to expect him to be responsible for a third control.

Matters have improved, too, from the cameraman's standpoint. On early versions of these dollies the cameraman's seat and the camera mounting were fixed to a central point at the front of the arm. When the cameraman wanted to pan through a wide angle and keep his viewfinder picture in sight throughout—which is a reasonable requirement—he had to press a pedal under one of his feet. This operated a motor which turned the cameraman's seat and the camera mounting together about their fixed point. At the completion of the movement the pedal had to be restored to a neutral position.

The cameraman's other foot rested on another pedal which controlled the raising and lowering of the arm of the dolly.

To the inexperienced, operating a camera on this type of dolly for the first time was a nightmare. It is not unusual to be asked to track out, pan, and vary the height, all at the same time. Only the highly skilled cameraman could signal his tracker, perform one movement with his left foot, a different movement with his right foot, pivot, focus, and correctly frame his picture simultaneously and instinctively.

The inexperienced cameraman could be forgiven for forgetting to do one or more of these things. Indeed, it was not unusual in these circumstances for such a cameraman to complete this complicated manoeuvre only to find that he had forgotten to operate one of the pedals, and that he and his camera were still rising rapidly into the over-hanging lamps.

Happily, later versions of this type of dolly are much easier to operate—probably due to pressure from frantic cameramen. Most of them now have a platform on which the cameraman can rest his feet, and which enables him to move his seat and camera mounting around a freely revolving pivot. The arm of the dolly can normally be raised or lowered by means of a twist-grip control mounted on the panning handle. These improvements led to a raising of the standard of work possible with a motorized dolly.

Since these dollies are motor driven, it is virtually impossible to bring the motor into play and switch it off, without a slight jerk. The cameraman must do his best to minimize this sudden movement which is liable to be transmitted to his camera at the beginning and end of each track. This can be done with practice, and it bears a direct relationship to the technique of anticipating signals to trackers.

Mole Richardson Crane

Some dollies must be operated by at least two trackers. The most common of these is the Mole Richardson Crane (see pp. 51 and 169).

It will be remembered that the camera and the cameraman are positioned at one end of an arm, which can pivot freely about a column mounted roughly in the centre of the dolly. The other end of this arm comprises a bucket into which lead weights are slotted to counterbalance the combined weight of the camera and the cameraman. The dolly is driven by an electric motor controlled by one of the trackers.

On early models the driver sat to the side of the dolly, and was solely responsible for driving the dolly forwards and backwards, and for controlling its speed. The "arm-swinger" stood on a platform at the rear of the dolly, and was responsible for all movement of the pivoted arm. A third tracker stood behind the dolly, and steered by means of a T-shaped handle which acted on the rear wheels.

The cameraman then had three trackers to control, and was faced with the unenviable task of attempting to give, on occasions, three different signals at once. When it is remembered that merely operating a camera mounted on a crane demands the utmost concentration from the cameraman, the standard of skill required can perhaps be realized.

The trackers had their problems, too. The driver and the steerer had to think as one man, and it often took many months of training before they could be brought to the necessary standard of competence. The arm-swinger, too, had to synchronize his movements with those of his team.

Despite all these difficulties this type of dolly was undoubtedly the most versatile of any in current use, and the camerawork accomplished with it was of a very high standard.

Later models are an improvement. On these the separate steerer has been eliminated, and the dolly is driven and steered by a tracker who stands on a low platform mounted behind the arm-swinger's platform. But improvements do not always seem to be immediately beneficial, and at first many drivers found difficulty in seeing the cameraman's signals. However, trackers soon developed their own methods of keeping the cameraman's hand constantly in sight, despite the very solid body of the arm-swinger who was less than two feet from their faces.

The cameraman was naturally pleased with this later model. The most important advantage was, of course, a reduction in the number of trackers under his control. The design of this crane also placed his two trackers close together, and the cameraman could direct his signals to that one area at the rear of the dolly. On earlier models the driver was some distance away from the swinger and to one side of the dolly, and synchronized signalling was sometimes virtually impossible.

Where more than one tracker has to be controlled, the cameraman must be especially meticulous with his signals. He must devise a method of signalling to individual trackers. These signals must be clear, and positive, leaving no doubt in the trackers' minds who is being signalled to do what.

Once again, there is no standard method of selective signalling. During his period as a tracker the cameraman must study other cameramen, and then formulate his own method of signalling before he is called upon to operate a camera in these circumstances.

His first attempts are likely to be unsuccessful. He may think that he is giving excellent signals to his trackers, but they in turn may well be confused by the vague and frantic flutterings of the cameraman's fingers. The inexperienced cameraman should listen to the advice of his trackers. They will know whether the cameraman's signals are clear and concise, and he should follow their suggestions.

Steadying the Camera

The type of dolly we have been discussing enables the camera to be used in versatile and exciting ways. But this can present the cameraman, particularly the inexperienced cameraman, with many problems.

His biggest early problem will be to find some means of keeping the camera absolutely steady. His seat can revolve freely through almost 360 degrees; his camera can be panned without regard to the movement of his seat; the arm of the crane is finely counter-balanced and will respond to the slightest movement—all these combine to counter his attempts to hold the camera steady.

Most mountings are provided with a tension-adjuster, however, usually in the shape of a small wheel near the cameraman's foot. If this adjustment is set too tight, the cameraman will have difficulty in moving his seat smoothly; if too slack, the seat will move to the slightest movement of the cameraman and he will have great difficulty in keeping his shots steady.

The cameraman should experiment with this tension-adjuster until it is set to be ideal for his particular method of operation. He will probably find that it is better to set the tension-adjuster a little too tight than a little too slack. He should not, however, tighten it to the point that smooth movement of the seat is impossible. If he experiments a little he will soon find the position to suit him personally.

The seat can normally be held in any position by means of a foot-brake operated by the cameraman. This is particularly useful when the cameraman wants to swing his seat from one position to another very quickly, and then wishes to steady himself immediately the new position has been reached. But the brake can also be used to steady the seat for static shots, and for helping to ensure that long, fast tracks are free from any sideways movement.

Ideally, the cameraman's seat should be in line with the camera at all times as this enables him to have an unobstructed view through his viewfinder. If the camera is swung through a wide arc, or even if a long pan is attempted, the cameraman can usually ease his seat around with the camera if the movement is conducted slowly.

But if the movement is to be a fast one, the cameraman will not have time to move his seat at the same speed as he moves the camera. If this is so, he must set the position of his seat and place his feet so that they will be in the correct position for the *end* of the movement. This is a similar technique to the one described in an earlier chapter on panning. The cameraman can get his legs into an awful tangle if he does not plan ahead in this manner.

When operating in these circumstances the cameraman must remember all he has learnt about pivoting, smooth tracking, and crabbing. This type of dolly, as we have said, is extremely versatile, and the movements the cameraman will be called upon to make about the set will be less inhibited and regular than those with a pedestal-mounted camera.

If he has developed a sound basic technique in all aspects of camera movement, he is likely to master this more advanced art very quickly. But no cameraman should be entrusted with this type of work until his basic technique is flawless. Sitting "up the front" of a crane is not the best place to learn focusing, framing, and pivoting.

As we saw in the chapter on equipment, there are various designs of camera dolly in current use, and they each require individual operating techniques. But they all present the cameraman with the same basic problem. At least one tracker must be controlled, and this must be done in such a way that they eventually act as one man.

This can be achieved only if the trackers are alert and skilful, and if the cameraman has acquired a high standard of technique. But, and this is probably the most important point, so much depends on the cameraman's ability to give clear, positive signals. Without these the camerawork will inevitably suffer.

Monitors for Trackers?

It is not really necessary to discuss each type of camera dolly separately, or to deal with the individual operating techniques called for. All the advice given above will apply to any camera dolly whatever its type or mode of operation. Having mastered the lay-out of the various controls, the cameraman is faced with the problem which is common to them all—the need to control his trackers by clear signals. It does not matter whether there is one tracker or six.

Should trackers be provided with miniature monitors mounted on their dollies? This is a favourite subject for discussion in television, and there are two schools of thought.

Trackers claim that a monitor would enable them to place the dolly in the ideal position for any shot with the minimum of signals from the cameraman. They point out that having seen a shot which the cameraman wants to frame, they could guarantee always to place the dolly in exactly the same spot however many times the shot is required. They stress the added advantage that slight adjustments of the dolly—to compensate for variations in the rehearsed positions of artists—can be accomplished instantly with no instructions from the cameraman.

Many cameramen, too, favour the use of monitors for trackers. They claim that these monitors help speed up rehearsals, reduce signalling to the barest minimum, and leave the cameraman free to concentrate on the finer aspects of his work. They agree that minor adjustments to the position of the dolly during transmissions are much smoother and less obtrusive.

There is no doubt that these arguments appear to be very sound. Certainly in the hands of an experienced team of cameraman and trackers a monitor can be an extremely useful provision.

But those who oppose the use of monitors for trackers are just as determined in their reasoning. They argue that the cameraman tends to leave his trackers to frame his shots for him. There is a danger that he will become lazy and dominated by his trackers. They stress the fact that trackers cannot look at monitors and the cameraman's hand at the same time, and that there is the very real danger that the cameraman's signals will be ignored.

The use of monitors would certainly encourage many a cameraman to leave most of the work to his trackers, and to settle for the

198

positions that they give him. Since most of his signals might well not be acted on by the trackers, the cameraman will tend to signal less and less. This can be a severe disadvantage to him if he is ever called upon to work on a camera dolly which has no monitor for the trackers. He will then be virtually in the position of a beginner, and he will have to re-learn the necessary technique. While he is doing so, his camerawork will be inferior to the standard required of him.

Further, his views on the framing of his shots may differ from those of the trackers. Although basic framing and composition should be common to all cameramen, the shot-problems facing the cameraman might well be too advanced for the trackers. The cameraman is invariably far more experienced than his trackers—indeed, many trackers have little experience of actual camerawork. They must be guided by the cameraman, and their function is to place the dolly where the cameraman wants it in order to frame each of his shots. And this is one of the strongest arguments against the provision of monitors for trackers. In inexperienced hands they can actually be a hindrance to the cameraman.

If trackers consulted monitors only occasionally in order to understand the cameraman's intentions, or to memorize the framing of the more difficult or vital shots, they could benefit from the provision of these monitors. But trackers are human, and soon they would tend to study the monitors more and more and the cameraman's signals less and less. Very gradually the cart would start to drive the horse.

Mirror Shots

Since part of the technique of television is concerned with the creation of a sense of reality where, perhaps, none exists, the cameraman is often involved in various forms of trick shots. These may involve the use of mirrors, special lenses, miniature models and so on. Although these types of shots are not often called for, they must be part of a cameraman's repertoire.

Mirrors (single, double, or multiple) are often used by directors for special effects. An extraordinary impression of height can be achieved by mounting a mirror above an artist or a scene, and shooting the reflections in the mirror.

Similarly, by mounting a mirror near the floor of the studio and shooting the reflection, the viewer can be led to believe that the artists are higher than they really are—on a high balcony for example.

These are typical examples of the use of single mirrors. But deciding on the correct siting of a mirror in order to obtain the effect required can seem to be anything but straightforward. The height at which it will be mounted, the angle of tilt, the distance from the lens, the lens to be used, and the size of the mirror, all have to be taken into account when lining up a shot of this nature.

Unless all these points are considered during the planning stage of a programme, and the necessary calculations made, there is a danger that valuable rehearsal time will be wasted in the studio. Lining up a mirror shot by hit or miss methods can take more time than the shot is probably worth.

And yet a basic knowledge of the principles of optics is all that is required to solve any problem connected with mirror shots. Light travels in a straight line, and the angle the incident ray makes with the mirror will equal the angle the reflected ray makes with the mirror on leaving it. The placing of the camera and the mirror to provide the required effect can easily be calculated from a scale drawing.

But the distance between the camera and the mirror, and the size of the mirror, depend very much on the angle of view of the lens to be used. Clearly, if a very wide angle lens is used, the mirror must either be very large, or it must be placed near the lens. But if the mirror is close to the lens, the full effect of using it is lost. And if a narrow-angle lens is used, there is not the same sense of depth and perspective as there would be with a wide-angle lens.

It follows, then, that where it is intended to use a mirror to add a feeling of height to a shot, it should be the largest obtainable. This not only allows wide-angle lenses to be used, but gives the cameraman a little more latitude in the framing of his shots.

When two mirrors are mounted roughly horizontally and facing each other—to act as a periscope—the width of the shot is dictated by the size of the mirror which first picks up the artist's reflection. Lining up a shot like this can be a time-wasting business. And when the positions of the mirrors in relation to each other are finalized, they must be carefully locked, and the camera position accurately marked.

However many mirrors are used in series to create a special effect in a shot, each additional mirror must be larger than the one which precedes it. How much larger will depend on the lens in use, and the physical distances involved.

There is one basic rule which beginners often forget when first

200

lining up a mirror shot. If the lens must be focused on the reflection in the mirror—which is invariably the case—the point of focus is equal to the distance from the camera to the mirror *plus* the distance from the mirror to the artist. A reflected image lies as far behind the mirror as the subject does in front. If the cameraman focuses on the mirror, all that will be in focus will be the mirror.

This point is really brought home to the cameraman when he is required to pan from the reflection of an artist in a mirror to the artist himself. Depending on the *f* stop in use, the amount of focus correction needed will usually be quite considerable—much more than the inexperienced cameraman might expect. A moment's thought will show why this is so, but many beginners flounder the first time they encounter this type of shot.

Correctly framing an artist's reflection in a mirror, and at the same time avoiding unwanted reflections, can be a tedious business. The slightest movement of the artist's head could take it out of the shot, or force the cameraman to move his camera to compensate. Moving the camera often brings unwelcome reflections of studio equipment or personnel into the shot, however, and the overall effect will hardly be what the director intended.

To ensure the success of this type of shot, the cameraman must enlist the help of the artist concerned. He must tell the artist to place his head so that he can always see the camera lens in the middle of the mirror. If the artist can see the lens, the lens can see him; and if the lens is in the middle of the artist's view of the mirror, he will be correctly framed in the shot.

Canted Shots

Directors sometimes ask for canted (or tilted) shots. Here the intention is to offer a shot which leans to one side. The floor, tops of doors, and all horizontal lines will no longer be parallel to the bottom of the frame. All vertical lines, although remaining at right-angles to horizontal lines, will be angled.

Used sparingly—certainly not more than two or three times in a major programme, and then only at the right time, and briefly—these shots can be very effective. An inexplicable feeling of excitement and life is conveyed, especially if the preceding and following shots are carefully selected.

Cameramen have used various methods to obtain this effect. Running one wheel of the dolly up a ramp is an unwise solution sometimes attempted. The camera is immobilized at this one spot, and the cameraman must try to control a leaning dolly and camera.

Apart from the fact that reaching a satisfactory position on the ramp can be a noisy operation, there is a certain amount of danger involved—the dolly could overturn.

Even where it is possible to achieve canted shots by rotating the camera tube, this is an unwise and cumbersome practice. It is far better to use proper optical devices, or mirrors. Technically undesirable, any interference with the camera tube leaves one with a misaligned and often inferior picture.

Lens Attachments

By far the best method is to use one of the many lens attachments which are available. These clamp on to the standard lenses, and have a moveable section which can be rotated to give any degree of tilt.

These special devices have many advantages. The cameraman can swing from normal to canted shots in a second or two. The angle of tilt is instantly variable—it can even be adjusted "in vision"—and the cameraman is in no way restricted by the requirements of these shots. When all the canted shots have been taken, the lens can be rotated to a horizontal position to act as a normal lens, or it can be quickly replaced by a standard lens at a suitable moment during the programme.

There are many of these special units available, each designed to produce various trick shots. Used sparingly, they can be quite amusing and effective, though there is a tendency among directors to overplay them. However, this is not the concern of the cameraman.

Again, special lenses can provide a split-image, multiple images—both static and moving—and even shots in which the subject lies in the centre of the frame surrounded by a circle of half a dozen images of itself. These images can be revolved around the central character, and there are occasions when this type of shot can be reasonably used—rare though they are.

Although only the very large television companies keep these lenses as standard equipment, other companies can usually hire them from the manufacturers, or from other companies. Bearing in mind the few occasions when they would be needed, this is probably the best method to be adopted by small studios.

Miniatures and Models

A shot of a model of a town, for example, rarely convinces the viewer that he is actually seeing a bird's-eye view of a real town.

Even allowing for the absence of life, there is a good reason for this.

If a camera were mounted on a hill overlooking a town, and a wide-angle lens used, the depth of field available would almost certainly encompass all that could be seen in the shot. The whole town would be in focus.

But when a shot is taken of a model, the camera is only a matter of feet away from it. Depending on the lens in use and the stop at which it is set, there is probably a restricted depth of field available. Some parts of the town are in focus, others are not. And it is this quality which detracts from the reality of the shot.

Whenever a cameraman is required to frame this type of shot, therefore, he must always arrange with the lighting director for the maximum amount of light to be thrown on the scene. He can then stop the lens down and increase the depth of field.

Camera movement about models and miniatures is more difficult to do well than when it is directed at full-size artists and scenes. Even though the depth of field may be fairly wide, the camera is invariably quite close to the model. Tracking in might bring the camera to within a foot or two of the subject, and the amount of focus correction needed might well be considerable. There is always the danger, too, that the shadow of the camera will be thrown on to the model.

All movement about models must be slow—except for special effects. Owing to the nearness of the camera, and the fact that wide-angle lenses are invariably used for this type of shot, changes in image size will be quite rapid even under normal circumstances. Fast moves are unnecessary.

The cameraman must be particularly careful to track smoothly and pivot accurately too. Since the subject is in miniature, slight movements of the camera will be exaggerated by the time the viewer sees the shot.

15

LIGHTING

THERE is no need for the cameraman to acquire a detailed knowledge of the techniques of television lighting. Cameramen are not responsible for placing lamps, controlling light levels, or the many other aspects of television lighting practice. These matters are the concern of the lighting director—or whatever title he is given from studio to studio. Lighting for television is a complicated and highly skilled job, and the techniques used are peculiar to this medium.

But good camerawork and lighting go hand in hand. No television cameraman can possibly consider himself skilled unless he is aware of the basic principles of television lighting. Without this knowledge he cannot use to the best advantage the lighting techniques employed on any television programme.

Necessity for Compromise

As we shall see later, the lighting director is rarely free to light a programme in such a way that every shot taken will be correctly and artistically lit. This is possible in filmed or video-taped productions, where each shot is treated individually. But a "live" television programme, once started, must run non-stop to its close, and there is no opportunity to light each shot separately before it is taken. Further, most scenes will probably be shot from a variety of angles, and by more than one camera.

The lighting director, therefore, must compromise drastically between the ideal and the practical. He must light each scene in such a way that close-ups, two-shots, group shots, and long shots can be taken from a multitude of angles, and these shots must all conform to the technical and artistic requirements of the medium.

But in every properly lit television scene there is always a "best" angle for close-ups or long shots; and there is always a "bad" angle which will produce technically unacceptable, inartistic, or downright ugly shots. Since cameramen are partly responsible for shooting-angles, and since they should be as keen as the

204

lighting director to produce attractive shots, it is obvious that learning something of the basic techniques of television lighting practice must be part of a cameraman's training.

The Purpose of Lighting

As long as there is light of some kind around, we will get pictures—of a sort! But unless this light is from an appropriate direction to suit subject and camera viewpoint, and of suitable quality and brightness, the result is liable to be quite unpredictable.

The lighting has simultaneously to fulfil several quite different functions. It must not be too bright, or light tones will blanch out. Too dim, and we cannot see shadow detail. At either extreme, picture defects arise. If its direction is wrong, the light creates uninteresting, misleading, or ugly effects. An object's appearance is spoiled, or an atmosphere destroyed. And all this for the variety of camera and subject positions the production director has decided to use.

We must throw light on to our subjects, then, if we are to produce an image on the camera tube. In that case, why not flood a scene with banks of frontal light which would cast soft shadows? This would eliminate many operational problems. We can answer this best by using an example.

Let us assume that we want to shoot a close-up of a man who is sitting in a chair. This chair is about nine feet in front of a stage-flat, and the camera is shooting from directly in front of our subject.

If we then flood our little scene from the front with half a dozen bright lights which have no directional properties, what would the image look like? The answer is that it would be flat and uninteresting, and there would be no depth to our shot.

It would be flat because the contours of the subject would cast no shadows, and his face would be a featureless, white blob. And there would be no depth to the shot because the subject would not be separated from the background. The overall effect would be very two-dimensional.

What we have really been saying is that the shot lacks contrast. In other words, if our picture is monochromatic and is a two-dimensional image of a three-dimensional subject, we must separate the various tonal values of our scene if we are to compensate for the loss both of colour and this third dimension.

Some parts of our shot will reflect more light than others. If we control the direction and intensity of the light falling on these varying reflective surfaces, we can control the reflected light from them and ensure that it falls within the contrast range of the tube. And we can also cause shadows to be thrown from the projecting features of our subject—his nose, chin, etc.—and begin to suggest that we really are shooting a three-dimensional scene.

Lamps fall into one of two rough categories; those that produce hard light, and those that produce soft light. Hard lamps throw light which is directional, and which casts hard shadows. The optical system is so designed that the light is concentrated over a small area to produce this effect.

Soft lamps on the other hand produce diffused light which is not directional, and which casts soft shadows. These lamps are often frosted to help originate this diffused light.

Although various terms have evolved for types of lighting equipment and the ways in which it is used, we shall find certain agreed fundamentals everywhere. Complete lighting treatment can be complex, employing a large number of lamps, each with a definite purpose (sometimes with dual functions), blending together to build their unified illusion. But quantity is not essential for quality. We may get brilliant results with a single lamp.

The basic lamp functions can be stated simply, as: the key light, the filler, back light, and the background light.

The Key Light

This is sometimes called the modelling light, and that is a clue to its purpose. The key light must be a hard light since it must throw hard shadows. These shadows reveal contours and texture. Shadowless light would suppress these features.

If we illuminate a table-tennis ball by placing our frontal light just beside the camera lens, we shall see it reproduced as a plain disc. But if we place a hard, directional light to one side of the ball, we begin to see its shape. The ball is brightly lit where it is nearest the light source, and becomes progressively darker for those parts farther away. The ball itself throws a shadow which suggests its three-dimensional nature.

In our original example, the key light throws shadows from such features as the artist's nose, chin, ears, eye-sockets and so on. He looks a little more three-dimensional. We know if he has a large nose or a double chin; just how much we learn depends on the direction and intensity of the key light.

Clearly a key light which is directed square-on to the artist's face (i.e. one which is mounted directly above our central camera position) is unsuitable if we are attempting to indicate the shape of our subject. Any shadows cast fall behind the subject and are not seen in our shot. The face is flat and featureless.

A key light mounted at an angle of 90 degrees to the centre line of our shot illuminates one side only of the artist. One half of his face is brightly lit; the other half is in shadow. This, too, is an unsuitable position for the key light.

On the other hand, if we mount the key light at an angle of 45 degrees to the centre line, we create what has been called a Rembrandt effect. This is named after the great Dutch artist who sometimes used this type of lighting arrangement. The most obvious result of Rembrandt lighting is a triangular highlight alongside the nose and under one eye—on that part of the face which is farthest from the key light.

In television, key lights are rarely mounted to give a Rembrandt effect. It is a little too severe for most television shots because it is rather inflexible. If the artist does not move and we shoot him from a carefully selected angle, the effect can be quite artistic. But these conditions do not apply to television, and a small movement of the artist or the camera can easily make the shot unattractive.

In fact this position of 45 degrees to the centre line is regarded by many lighting directors as the maximum limit for the position of the key light. Most of them favour a point somewhere between a Rembrandt and a frontal approach—i.e. between 20 and 30 degrees to the centre line.

The ideal vertical angle at which the key light should look down at the artist is approximately 30 degrees to the horizontal, though this is not always possible to achieve.

The intensity of light falling on a subject is measured in foot candles. Although we need not go into light measurement in this chapter, we can say that 1 foot candle is the intensity of light given off by 1 candle and measured at a distance of 1 foot. The average intensity of light falling on a subject from a key light is normally between 60 and 80 foot candles. This is not a firm rule, because a lot depends on the types of tube in use. Even such considerations as the comfort of the artist have a bearing on the intensity of the key light.

But when lighting directors are balancing the intensity of the various lights they employ to illuminate a scene, the majority of them keep the intensity of the key light constant and experiment with the intensity of the fillers, back lights, and background lights in order to obtain the effect they want.

As we have said, the key light is a hard lamp. And hard lamps can be "flooded" or "spotted"—that is, the light from them can be either spread or directed along a narrow beam as required. Key lights are normally set at "full flood", but they can be "spotted" if they fail to provide the required intensity at the subject. This may happen if the lamps are a great distance away from the scene, or if they have lost some of their intensity because of age.

Filler

So far we have placed a hard, directional key light to one side of our subject. This has cast dark shadows and given us some idea of his shape and features. But these shadows are too severe. We need to direct a softer light at these dark areas to soften the shadows and reveal the detail they are hiding. In other words, we want to reduce the contrast range in the shot and illuminate the shadows without creating additional shadows. That is the function of the filler.

Obviously, we use a soft lamp—more accurately soft lamps, because filler light usually takes the form of two or more soft light sources.

These are mounted on the opposite side of the subject to the key light and at about the same horizontal angle (that is, 20 to 30 degrees to the centre line). Because of the different nature of the filler light, however, this angle is nothing like as critical as the angle of the key light.

The intensity of filler light varies considerably, but 30 and 60 foot candles is typical for IO monochrome cameras.

Back Light

We have lit our subject so that his features and three-dimensional shape are obvious. We must now separate him from the background if we are to show that he is not sitting against it. We do this by mounting a hard light behind and above him, and directed in such a way that his shoulders and his head are given a rim of light revealing edge contours and depth.

The vertical angle of the back light is rather important. If it is too shallow, it might strike the lens of the camera and cause flaring. If it is too steep it will strike protruding features on the front portion of the subject, highlighting them and distracting from any careful attempts at modelling.

The ideal vertical angle for the back light is about 45 degrees, and the intensity of the light can vary considerably—from 60 to 100 foot candles is a rough guide for the IO monochrome camera.

Background Light

Lamps directed specifically on to the setting are called background, set, or setting lights. They serve to create an illusion of scale, space, solidity; to build up a particular mood or environment; to cause subjects to stand out from their surroundings.

Its intensity varies according to the tone of the background itself and the subject's inherent tonal range. But it should never make the background appear brighter than the artist's face. This rule is disregarded when special lighting effects are required—the most familiar example of this being a silhouette.

Hard lamps are used to provide background light, and they are normally "fully flooded". The tonal values of backgrounds can vary so greatly that it is impossible to give any indication of light values.

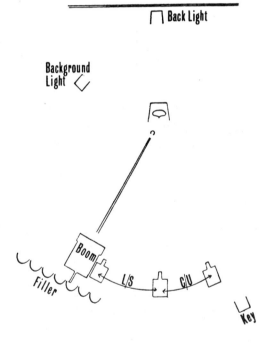

Fig. 61. Simple, basic arrangement of four lights about a static subject.
Note: (a) C.U.s should be attempted only from along the arc drawn between the key light and the centre line.
(b) Long-shots may be attempted from as far round as the filler.
(c) Boom placed on filler side of artist.

Types of Lamps

Before going on to discuss more complicated lighting arrangements, the cameraman might appreciate a few words here about the equipment the lighting director uses in a television studio. We cannot be specific when dealing with equipment, however. The actual make and style of lamps varies throughout the world, and some types of lamps are never seen in some television studios.

But we can generalize in the sense that we can look at typical light values of lamps in common use, and mention their function in the lighting director's plan of operation.

The smallest lamp normally used in monochrome is the "dinkie" ("inkie dink"), of 150 watts. It is used in confined spaces, and its light is directional in nature. It is useful for clamping on to the tops and sides of sets because it is small and light. A handy little lamp, then, for lighting that awkward corner or partly obscured flat, where its low output is acceptable.

The "pup"—500 or 1000 watts—is the bigger brother of the "inkie". It is used in the same circumstances—in confined spaces, or when highly directional, readily controllable light is required. But it delivers a stronger light, and is useful in situations where an "inkie" would be inadequate.

The "2K"—so called because of its output of 2 kilowatts—is probably the most widely used lamp in television. It is a hard lamp and is directional in effect. This lamp is admirably suitable either as a key light, back light, or background light. In fact it is the best general-purpose hard light in universal use in monochrome studios.

As a rough guide to its properties, it will illuminate an area 10 ft. by 10 ft. to a level of 60 foot candles if it is placed about 20 ft. from a subject. This can vary according to the age and condition of the lamp, of course, but it is a rough rule-of-thumb for general purposes. Newer, tungsten-halogen lamps can double these figures.

The "5K", 5,000 watts, is the big brother of the "2K". They are both used in similar circumstances, but the "5K" is preferred when a high level of light intensity is required. It is also used on outside locations to provide a filler effect against deep shadows cast by strong sunlight. In colour studios it is widely applied.

The "10K", 10,000 watts, is merely an extension of the "5K" and is rarely used in smaller television studios.

The soft lamps used as fillers are invariably frosted or opal in nature to provide the required diffused source for the light. They virtually cast no shadows, and their intensity varies according to the requirements of the shot and the intensity of the hard lights in use on the scene. They are usually mounted in multiples of 500 or 1,000 watts according to the intensity of filler light required.

Controlling the Area Illuminated

"Barn Doors" and "French Flags" are projections placed in front of lamps by lighting directors to control the areas illuminated by them.

This is sometimes necessary when the lighting director does not want a beam of light to fall on certain areas in its path. We need not concern ourselves with his reasons here.

According to the effect he wants he will use either a "Barn Door" or a "French Flag".

"Barn Doors" consist of pieces of metal mounted around the periphery of the lamp, and hinged so that they can be set at any angle. Since they are close to the actual light source, they provide a soft edge to the light where they cut the beam. The light does not end abruptly—it tapers away unnoticed.

The "French Flag" consists of an adjustable arm carrying a rectangular metal plate, which can be mounted in front of a lamp and at varying distances from it. It cuts off the light in a sharper manner than the "Barn Door" therefore. This is particularly useful when the area of set which must be excluded is very near the area which must be illuminated by the lamp.

Controlling Lamp Intensity

Finally we can look at a rather interesting way in which the lighting director controls the intensity of his lights.

If we imagine that a lamp is pointing at an angle of 45 degrees to the floor of a set, it is obvious that the part of the floor nearest the lamp is brighter than the part farthest away. The amount by which the intensity of light varies from front to back depends on such considerations as the distance of the lamp and the angle it makes with the floor.

But if the lighting director wants an even level of light intensity over the whole area, he inserts what is called a "wire" or "jelly" in front of the lamp. This is simply a wire mesh suspended in a gelatine compound, and it reduces the intensity of the light passing through it.

By experimenting with the size, number, and position of these "wires" he can achieve a carefully graded intensity of light falling over an area from one lamp.

In our example, he would concentrate the effect of his "wires" towards the bottom of the lamp, and grade them until they were not obstructing the light emanating from the top of the lamp at all.

Lighting Arrangements

The lighting director's work becomes more complicated if more people are involved in a scene, particularly if a variety of shots is to be taken. Let us look at typical lighting arrangements for straightforward two-shots and three-shots covered by three cameras and then at planned and unlimited artist movement.

Fig. 62. Interview two-shot for three cameras. Lamp (Ka) is the key light for artist A, and lamp (Kb) is artist B's key light. The filler light is common to both artists, and they are each lit with their individual back lights—(b1a) and (b1b) respectively.

Some lighting directors would use artist A's key light to serve as artist B's back light, and dispense with separate back lights altogether. This is an economical method of lighting this type of shot, and it is often seen in television studios.

But many lighting directors use individual back lights whenever possible. They maintain that this enables them to balance the lighting on each individual artist. This is true, of course, but it is not always convenient or practical.

The background lights have not been included in the diagram, since they do not directly concern us here.

If we look at the diagram we can see that the relationship between key light (Ka), artist A and filler is similar to that in Fig. 61. Camera One is ideally placed for shooting close-ups of artist A, providing these are taken from somewhere within the arc drawn between the filler and key light (Ka). The best close-ups, in fact, will be those taken with the camera placed not more than about 25 degrees to the key light.

Clearly all that has just been said applies to close-ups of artist B taken with Camera Three. Camera Two should confine itself to two-shots and wide shots, though close-ups of either artist can be attempted *provided neither artist looks at this central camera.*

In this type of lighting arrangement the two key lights should never make an angle with each other which is less than 180 degrees—measured on the camera side of the diagram. The main reason for this is to avoid the danger of the artists receiving two nose shadows. The back lights must be directly behind each artist's head in relation to the position of the respective close-up camera. As we indicated earlier, the boom should work from the area around the filler. In this example it can be placed on either side of Camera Two.

Fig. 63. Three-shot covered by three cameras. Once again each artist has been provided with an individual back light, but the arrangement of key lights is rather interesting.

Key light (K1) serves artist A, and it is also the key light for artist B when he is looking at artist C. Similarly, key light (K2) serves artist C, and also artist B when he is looking at artist A.

The position of Camera One should make the same angle with key light (K2) as in our previous examples. It can then shoot close-ups of artist C, and also of artist B when he is looking at artist A.

Camera Two should again be restricted to wide shots. It should never be used to provide close-ups of artist B, unless he is looking towards either of the side artists.

Wide shots may be taken from anywhere within the 180-degree arc drawn between the key lights, in fact. The two side cameras, therefore, can provide the fullest range of shots possible in this scene.

As before, the boom must work from the filler area, and if there is a necessity for the use of two booms they can be placed each side of Camera Two.

212

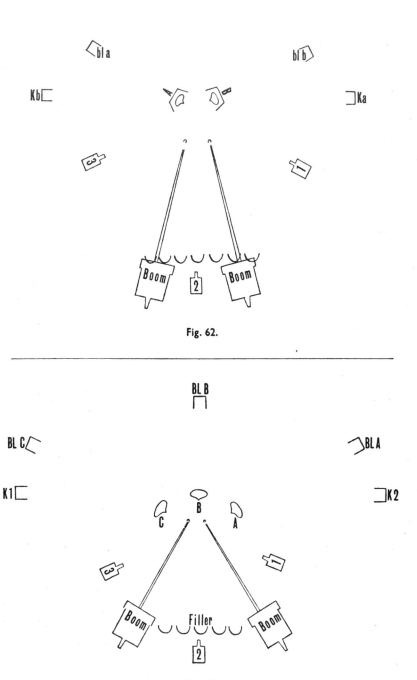

Fig. 62.

BL B

BL C

BL A

K1

K2

C   B   A

Boom   Filler   Boom

2

Fig. 63.

Fig. 64. Planned artist movement covered by four cameras. The examples we have considered so far have been fairly straightforward. The artists have not moved, and there have been no difficult problems to solve.

But when artists move about a set, the lighting director must ask certain questions before he can decide where to place his lamps. Where will the artist stand before making the move, and what are the shots that will be taken of him at this point? Where does he move to, and will boom coverage be needed during this movement? Where does the move end, and what shots will be taken of him there?

Having obtained the answers from the director, he can prepare a lighting plan to ensure that the scene is correctly lit for all these shots.

Before discussing the lighting methods used, let us examine in greater detail the moves and camera shots.

The artist stands at position A in a medium long shot, taken with Camera One. The director then cuts to a close-up on Camera Two for a few seconds, then back again to the wide shot on Camera One.

The artist crosses to the window in this wide shot, and looks out (position B). The director cuts to a close-up of the artist on Camera Four. As the artist faces into the room again (position C) the director cuts to a wide shot on Camera Two. The artist moves forward in this wide shot and sits on a chair (position D). A close-up of the artist is taken here on Camera Three.

We can now look at each of these shots in turn, and study the way in which each has been lit.

At position A his key light will be lamp (a), his back light lamp (b,, and his filler (f I). Note that the close-up camera must be Camera Two since it is nearer the key light than Camera One.

As the artist crosses to position B, his key light is still lamp (a) for part of the move. As he nears the window, however, he walks into key light (d). His back light for the move is lamp (c).

He looks out of the window. His key light is lamp (e), his back light lamp (d), and his filler (f 2). Again note the nearness of the close-up camera to the key light.

As he faces into the room again (position C) his key light is lamp (d), his back light lamp (e), and his filler (f I).

As he walks to position D and sits, his key light is still lamp (d), his back light is lamp (f) for the latter part of his walk and for his position when sitting, and his filler is (f I) as before. The close-up camera (Camera Three) is the camera nearest the key light (d).

The boom should work from beneath the filler—as mentioned in the previous examples—where there should be no danger of the boom shadows being seen in any of these shots.

This example shows how the lighting director arranges his lamps to serve dual purposes. Lamp (e), for example, is a key light, for the artist at position B, and a back light for him at position C. But if we look at the lighting arrangement for each individual shot we can see that the relative positions of the key light, back light, and filler are the same as in our very first example. And it is the camera which is nearest the key light which must always be the one that shoots the close-ups.

Fig. 65. Unlimited artist movement covered from many camera angles. The squares within the lit area which have been lettered A to F indicate the rough areas covered by the lamps of the same respective letters. Area B, then, is lit both by lamp (b) and lamp (bI). As we mentioned in an earlier example, these two lamps must never make an angle with each other which is less than 180 degrees on the camera side of the diagram. Depending on the position of the artist and the direction from which a shot is taken, each lamp can function either as a key light or a back light.

There are certain limitations, however, on the type of shots which may be taken from certain areas.

In the first place, wide shots may be taken from anywhere within the area bounded by X–Y. The shaded area near the filler lights, however, is unsuitable for close-ups, unless the artist is looking towards one of the key lights. This point has been made before in earlier examples.

But if the close-ups are confined to the unshaded areas between X–Y, the artist will always have a key light, back light, and filler light when he is facing the camera.

The boom must once again work from the region of the filler. Its shadows will then always fall towards the camera taking the shot, and they will not be seen.

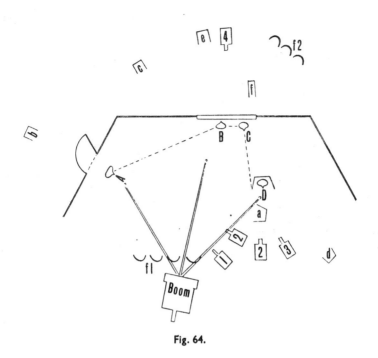

Fig. 64.

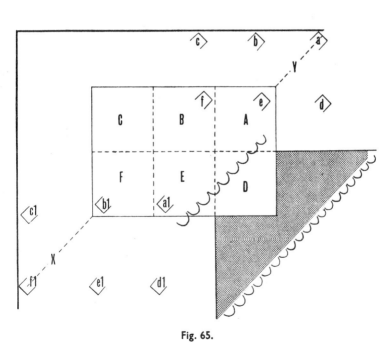

Fig. 65.

215

Fig. 66. Director's floor-plan for major show. We can now look at the way in which a lighting director lights a major show. We can study the positions of his lamps, and if we remember the principles laid down in our previous examples we should be able to understand why they are placed where they are.

We shall see, too, how the basic rules are sometimes "bent" a little for practical reasons, and a few of the devices employed by lighting directors to overcome some of the problems of a programme of this nature.

We shall not discuss the position of every artist, the shots from every camera angle, or the full lighting arrangement used on this particular programme. Instead we shall look at the lighting director's general lighting rig for the main areas, and then single out certain individual areas which needed a special treatment.

In an attempt to avoid overcomplicating the diagram the artists' positions have been excluded. But the plan shows the main areas of action, and the camera positions adopted to cover this action.

The programme was a light-musical show with a winter setting. The area at the top of the diagram was a ramp representing a sleigh-run (areas A–B) and this sloped down from A to B. The haycart (D) stood under a slatted roof, which was patched here and there with straw.

Just below the centre line of the drawing (E)—running from right to left—stood a series of flats representing the exterior of a large house. Below these flats the settings represented the interior of this house (F).

This interior was covered by a roof which sloped downwards from (F) to (E).

That, very simply, was the set. From a floor-plan such as this—and with information on the positions the artists would adopt throughout the show—the lighting director prepared a plan on which he marked the position for each lamp he would use on the programme (see Fig. 67).

Fig. 67. Lighting director's plan for major show. Before explaining the function of the lamps marked it must be pointed out that we shall not study every lamp used on the programme. Instead, we shall look only at those lamps which have been identified by letters and numbers. The system of marking the lamps followed the simple code: K. = Key light, B = Back light, F = Filler light. We shall refer to Fig. 66 for the camera positions, and to Fig. 67 for the lighting arrangements and artists' positions.

The main action started with children climbing on to their sledges at the top of the ramp (A), and sliding down on them to the base of the ramp (B). The action was shot by Camera Two (on position 2C) with cut-away shots on Camera Three (position 3A).

Four key lights were used to light this ramp area; lamps K1, K2, K3, and K4. The corresponding back lights were lamps B1, B2, B3, and B4. Fillers F1, F2, and F3 provided the filler light for the ramp area, though it can be seen that they also served as general purpose filler light for the whole of the set to the top half of our diagram.

As the children congregated at the base of the ramp (B), Camera Two moved to position 2B, and then tracked in to position 2A. Camera One took up position 1C. The sound on this item had been pre-recorded and no boom was required.

Let us look at the lighting arrangement employed for this position at the base of the ramp. Lamp K5 became the key light when the children moved out of the range of lamp K4. Similarly, lamp B5 became the back light for the area not covered by lamp B4.

Since the next movement of the children would be into the floor area (C), to the right of the ramp, the lighting director devised a lighting arrangement to accommodate this movement.

He mounted lamps K6, K7, K8, and K9 as his key lights, and lamps B6 and B7 as his back lights. Fillers F1, F2, and F3 still served as general purpose filler lights for this area.

Note that lamp B6 is larger than the other back lights. In fact it is a "5K" lamp, and it was used to reduce the risk of multiple shadows which might have resulted had a number of "2K" lamps been used instead.

Camera Three was not used for close-ups in this area—since it was near the filler side of the lighting scheme. Camera One shot close-ups from positions 1C and 1D and Camera Two (positions 2A and 2B) was also used for close-ups when they were called for. Ideally the boom should have worked from near the filler, but the con-

216

gestion on the floor forced it to the left. The boom operator had to be very alert to prevent unwanted shadows.

The standing lighting arrangement of key lights from the left and filler from the right—used up to this point in the show—was reversed for the covered area in front of the haycart (D).

This was necessary because the boom had difficulty in working along the wall near the fillers, and it was forced to the left of Camera Two (on position 2C). In this position, the boom was directly in the path of the key lights mounted to the left of this area, and boom shadows would have been inevitable.

The lighting director overcame this by mounting lamp K10 to act as key light for this area, filler F4 to serve as the filler light, and lamps B8 and B9 as his back lights. In fact, lamp B8 was half back light and half effects light, since it shone through the slatted roof setting the mood of this scene—which represented the Nativity.

Camera Two was used for general shots because it was near the filler, and Camera Three (position 3B) was used for close-ups.

It can be seen that the principles of lighting—and restricting camera angles to conform to them—which we discussed for simpler layouts still applied here. In fact each scene was regarded as an entity in itself, and was illuminated with the standard arrangement of key light, back light and filler—and these lights bore the same relative positions to each other as they did in our very first example.

An interesting problem presented itself when an artist stood in the doorway of the house (E) and sang into Camera Two (position 2C).

Lamp K11 was the main forward key light for the exterior of the house, and lamp B10 the backlight. But Camera Two was directly in the line of the key light K11, and its shadow would be seen in its own shot.

For this particular item the lighting director faded out lamps K11 and B10 entirely and mounted lamps K12 and B11 (shining through the doorway) to serve as his key light and back light respectively. Similarly he faded out filler F3 and mounted filler F5 to act as his filler light. The boom worked from the direction of this filler—that is, to the left of Camera Two.

The scene was then lit by a key light, back light, and filler in the normal way, and the risk of shadows was eliminated.

The interior set—in the lower half of our diagram—was extremely difficult to light well. The pitched roof prevented lamps being mounted on the gantries in the normal way, and lamps had to be attached to the beams running across the underside of this roof.

The difficulties encountered in physically attaching the lamps to the set added to the problem of lighting a covered area, and the diagram shows that the lighting director was forced to use "pups" and "inkies" as his key lights and back lights in many cases.

The scene was meant to represent a late-nineteenth-century farmhouse interior, so the overall lighting effect was low-key in nature. The key lights were "pups" K13, K14, K15, K16, K17, and "inkie" K18—which was hidden behind the pillar of the door. Back lights were "2K"s, namely lamps B12 and B13, and lamps F6 and F7 provided the filler light.

As a general rule close-ups were taken from the left of the set, and the boom worked to the right of the filler.

The artist standing near the fireplace (F) presented some problems. With the general lighting arrangement for this area there was a danger of boom shadows, and, to some extent, camera shadows from Camera Three (position 3C).

For this reason the shot was lit separately in the following way. Lamp K19 became the key light, lamp B14 the back light, and F6 remained as the filler light.

Since the boom had to work to the right of Camera Three, it was breaking the rules by working down the line of the key light. This could not be avoided, however, and the cameraman was forced to frame his shot in such a way that the area to the left of the artist (looking from the direction of the camera) was not included in the shot. This was the area in which the boom shadow fell.

In fact the artist was framed in M.C.U. throughout the item, and the lighting arrangement worked very well.

Continued on page 222

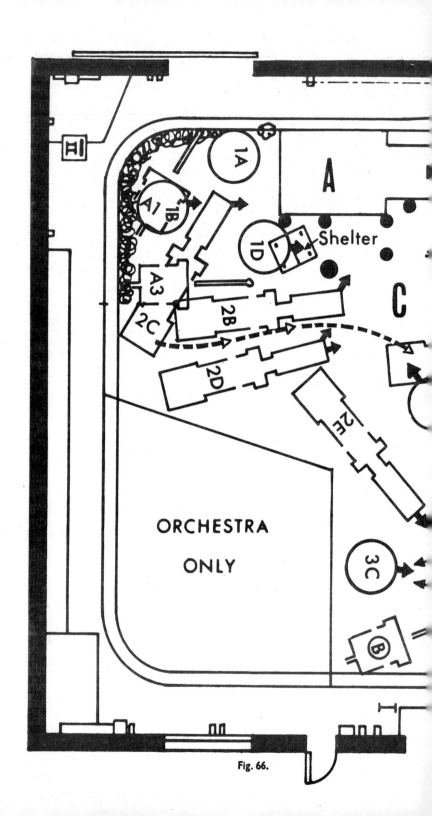

Fig. 66.

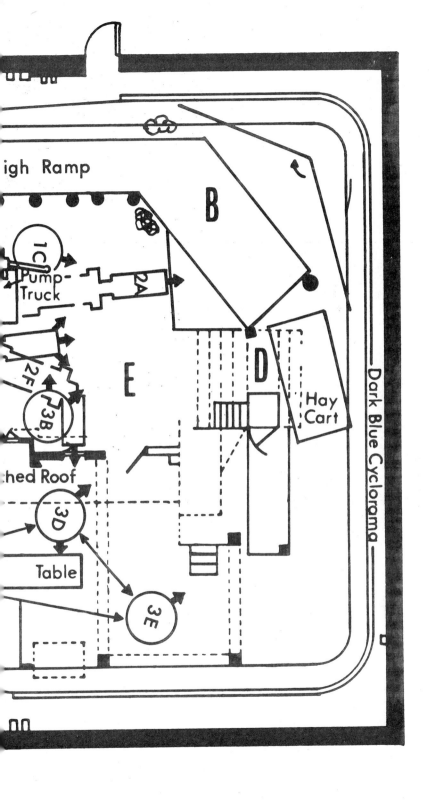

igh Ramp

B

1C

Pump-
Truck

2A

2F

E

D

3B

Hay
Cart

hed Roof

3D

Table

3E

Dark Blue Cyclorama

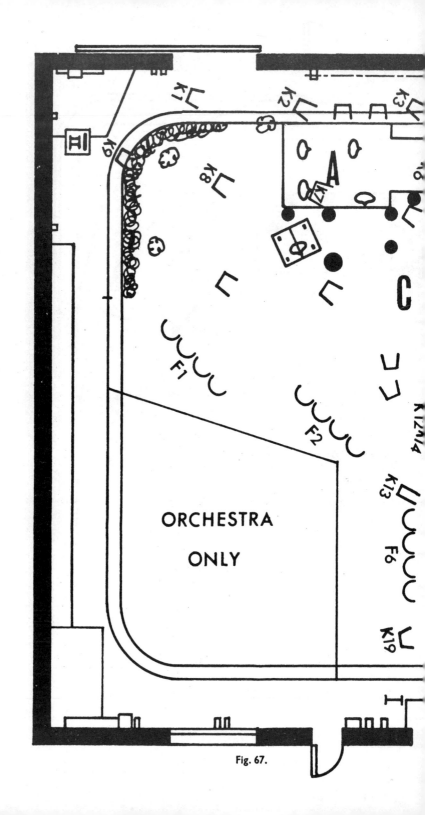

Fig. 67.

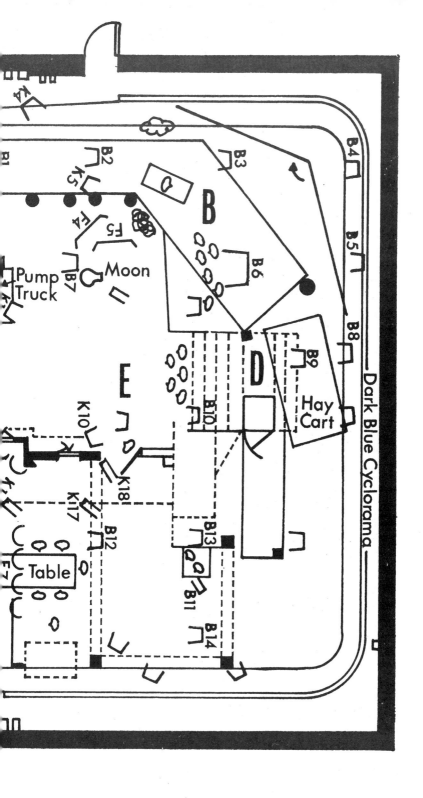

A number of lamps on the diagram have not been mentioned or marked in any way. This was done deliberately to avoid complicating the study of the lighting rig. But the function of every light can be easily calculated by studying its position in relation to other lamps, and by noting the position of the artists marked on the diagram.

In its final form the lighting plan might appear to be very complicated at first glance. But as we have shown, if the scenes are taken individually the plan is quite easy to follow.

The positions of some of the lamps were altered slightly during rehearsals to accommodate some changes in artist movement, and in cases where set-dressings prevented cameras and booms taking up their planned positions on the floor as shown on the plan.

But these alterations were minor in nature, and the show was transmitted with the lighting arrangement seen here.

Back Projection

We cannot dismiss the subject of lighting without looking at some of the special effects used in television. A knowledge of some of these techniques is necessary to give the cameraman an all-round awareness of matters that have some bearing on camera-work.

Back-projection consists of a screen placed behind an artist, on to which still or moving pictures are thrown by a projector to provide economic, flexible scenery, or extensions to settings. This projector is placed behind the screen—that is, on the other side of the screen to the artist—hence the term back-projection.

It has many advantages from the director's and designer's point of view. Still pictures are produced by inserting slides into the projector, and since these can be changed within seconds one area of the studio can be used for a variety of different scenes. Small changes of foreground objects and set-dressings—to synchronize with these slide changes—can quickly and easily transform a scene.

When a film is run through the projector, an amazing impression of reality is conveyed to the viewer. A typical example of the use of moving back-projection is the changing countryside seen through the window of a train. Without this facility it is difficult to convince the viewer that the artists really are in a railway carriage.

But let us look at this special effect from a lighting standpoint. In the first place the lighting director must keep frontal light off the screen if the projected images are to be seen clearly by the camera—and ultimately by the viewer. Yet he must continue to provide artists who stand in front of the screen with key light and filler light—both frontal lights.

222

How is he to prevent these lights falling on the screen and dimming the images? The obvious solution is to mount the screen so far behind the artist that these frontal lights cannot fall on it. But the farther the screen is moved away from the camera, the bigger it must be. And the room behind the screen must be increased to enable the projector to throw a larger picture.

This solution is not always possible, therefore, because space in a television studio is often limited. But many lighting directors use an interesting technique to overcome the problem of unwanted frontal light when the screen must be close to the artist. They move the artist's frontal lights very close to him, and reduce the intensity of the light emanating from these sources.

The light intensity of the screen depends on the equipment used. The brighter the image, the more expensive the equipment. But the screen should never be brighter than the artist's face—though even the most expensive equipment rarely produces these circumstances.

If the screen is not very bright—which is more often the case—the lighting director can lower the intensity of all his light falling on the artist, and request that the apertures of the lenses be opened up. This helps to reduce the difference between the intensity of the artist's lights and the brightness of the screen. But opening up the aperture reduces the depth of field available, and the screen must not be so far behind the artist that it falls outside this depth of field.

Cameramen must remember that they must place their cameras at right-angles to back-projection screens. And they must avoid at all costs shooting the edges of this screen. The viewer wants to believe that he is looking at a tropical scene through a bamboo window frame—not a film of it projected on to a screen.

Background Effect

Metal stencils can be inserted in projector lamps or hung before spotlights to enable patterns and images to be thrown on to the scenic backcloth or flats. These break up what might otherwise be a plain, uninteresting background, and they can sometimes be used to create mood in a scene without the use of sets.

There are disadvantages to such front projection. Spill light dilutes the effect; patterns stay in the lamps for the duration of a programme. If a cluster of lamps carrying slides is mounted above a set, and the lamps switched on and off to provide various combinations of images, the scenes can be varied quite dramatically.

These changes are sometimes made during a shot to provide

exciting transformations in vision, and this technique has been developed to a very high degree by certain lighting directors. Light entertainment shows, in particular, are excellent programmes with which to experiment, and the results invariably justify the time and effort involved.

16

OUTSIDE BROADCASTS

THE work of an outside broadcast unit (or OB unit for short) might seem to the layman to be more exciting and interesting than television studio operations. And there are occasions when he would probably be right. OBs release the crews from the confines of the studio, and take them to new and challenging venues all over the country.

But for every cameraman who loves OB work, there is one who hates it. And those who dislike it regard as disadvantages the very things that appeal to those who love it.

The constant travelling, the varying conditions which exist at the site, the constant need to compromise the desirable with the available, the outdoor work in all types of weather, the lack of rehearsals and the uncertainty of transmissions, the hours between rigging the equipment and shooting the programme when there is nothing to do—all these circumstances, and dozens more, provide individuals with reasons for liking or disliking OB work.

A little girl is reputed to have asked, "Mummy. Is daddy dead?" To which the mother replied, "No, dear. He's an OB cameraman."

Clearly, regular OBs are probably more suited to single men, but this is a personal matter and hardly justifies further discussion here!

Whatever its merits or demerits, however, OB work has a technique all its own. And there is no doubt that it presents the cameraman with an exciting challenge and many interesting problems.

His work will take him to village halls, swimming pools, golf courses, race tracks, and many other unlikely sites for television programmes. Some of these venues might well be far removed from normal services, and the unit must carry its own power supplies in case they are needed.

Much of the cameraman's time will be spent in travelling to a

225

location, and rigging and de-rigging his equipment. On many OB units he is expected to share the heavy work of lifting the cameras and other camera equipment on to high platforms, though on some units this work is done by a team of riggers.

The cameras used are normally the lightest available, therefore, and they are invariably supplied with waterproof jackets to protect them from wet weather. The crews, too, must be supplied with protective clothing, because they are expected to work in all types of weather throughout the year.

The success of an OB depends very much on the correct siting of the cameras; in most cases they can rarely be moved once they have been rigged. Planning is a team operation, involving the director, planning engineers, senior video engineers, lighting directors and sometimes the senior camera and sound men.

The siting of the cameras depends to a large extent on the range of lenses available, and we shall discuss OB lenses later in the chapter.

Many OBs—football matches, processions, races, boxing matches and so on—follow a fairly regular, definable pattern; although details can change unpredictably from moment to moment. The lack of rehearsals and finality of transmissions, however, provide the cameraman with interesting opportunities to prove his worth.

He often has the responsibility of selecting the optimum shots from his viewpoint. The OB director is very much in the hands of his cameraman, and it is often their skill and initiative alone that is responsible for the success of an OB.

No director can tell a cameraman in advance whether a batsman in cricket or baseball will hit the next ball to his left or right, or whether he will hit it at all. And if he does hit it, only the speed of the cameraman's reflexes will keep the ball in the shot. No cameraman worth his salt can resist such a challenge, and this utter dependence of the director on the cameraman is one of the most satisfying features of OB camerawork.

Before going on to more technical matters, it is worth mentioning the bond which grows up between the members of an OB unit. Perhaps it springs from the fact that they share the hardships and discomforts which are part and parcel of OB work. Perhaps it is due to the fact that they spend much of their off-duty hours in each other's company. Whatever the reason, it is there, and probably explains why many OB personnel could never be persuaded to work anywhere else.

Equipment

More often than not, once a camera has been placed in position for an OB it stays there. For this reason the camera mountings are normally less versatile than studio mountings, though most OB units carry at least one lightweight, trackable dolly.

The most common type of camera mounting is a simple tripod, having telescopic legs which can be clamped in any position, enabling the camera to be set at almost any height. These legs are normally equipped with a spiked end, which can be driven into a wooden platform, for example, and which help to prevent the legs splaying under the weight of the camera.

As an additional safeguard against splaying, the legs are often held when in the standing position by a strap which passes through each leg in turn. Some cameramen always insist that a piece of wood, with a triangular portion cut away, is placed against the foot of each leg and nailed to the platform. These are commonly called "crow's feet", and they certainly render the collapse of the tripod extremely unlikely.

Equally common on OB units is the Moy-base, which consists of a strong metal column resting on its own, stable base. Some versions of this type of mounting enable the height of the camera to be adjusted quite easily by merely turning a handle.

If the cameras must be moved during an OB—particularly on indoor programmes—the most satisfactory type of mounting is one of the many makes of lightweight dollies specially designed for OB work. These normally have four wheels (some with pneumatic tyres to contend with the uneven floors that are often met with), a seat for the cameraman, and a steering device which acts on the two rear wheels.

They can be moved around with little effort, and are pleasantly quiet. Most of them have some provision for varying the height of the camera, though the type of mechanism installed does not usually enable these changes of height to be made smoothly when the camera is on the air.

Simple movements can be attempted by fitting the tripod, which we mentioned earlier, on to a three-wheeled, triangular, tubular base, known as a "skid". This can be pushed around the floor by the cameraman, though it is difficult to control the direction of movement very precisely. The wheels revolve freely (rather like castors) and are independent of each other; unless the cameraman is forceful with his tracking, the skid is inclined to go where it wants.

As a basic lens complement, OB cameras are invariably equipped with the standard range of lenses found on studio cameras. Their work often takes them indoors, where the distances involved will be similar to those met with in a studio. But since the cameras are also required to be used on outdoor events, where they might be hundreds of yards from the subjects they are shooting, there is a real need for very long focal length lenses; or, better still, zoom lenses.

Using the Zoom Lens

The zoom lens is the most useful piece of equipment the cameraman could wish for on an outdoor OB. The reasons are obvious. In the majority of cases the camera positions are static and ordinary lenses place limitations on the flexibility of the television coverage. The biggest disadvantage with ordinary lenses is that they provide little opportunity for the director to move us closer to some point of interest on the screen.

Let us imagine an OB at a motor-racing circuit, and that the director is taking a medium long shot of the field hurtling through a bend—on Camera Two, say. Suddenly, one of the cars spins and leaves the track. The director wants the viewer to see this exciting happening in close-up—but he cannot track his camera closer to the scene.

If no zoom lenses are being used, he must cut to another shot to enable Camera Two to change to a long focal length lens. By the time the director has cut back to this tighter shot the car might well have regained the track. The viewer will be left wondering why the director cut to a shot of another part of the circuit just when something exciting was happening in front of him.

Had Camera Two been fitted with a zoom lens, however, this unsatisfactory situation would never have arisen. As the car left the track, the cameraman could have zoomed in to give the viewer a close-up of the spinning car, and of the driver's efforts to extricate himself from his predicament.

There would have been no necessity for the director to cut away to another shot—perhaps an irrelevant shot—in order to show the event in close-up on Camera Two. And when the car regained the track, the cameraman could have zoomed out to include the rest of the field, and panned them to the point where the next camera would take over the coverage.

The zoom lens, then, enables the director to maintain continuity in his directing, and provides him with the facility to single out items of interest for the viewer in an immediate, logical manner.

It offers more scope to the cameraman in the range of his camerawork too. Nothing is more exasperating for a cameraman than to know that the shot calls for movement, or a longer focal length lens, and to be helpless to provide this facility.

There are so many occasions when the cameraman must allow badly composed shots to be taken on his camera because he is not equipped with a zoom lens, and his camera position is fixed. He might be framing two people who are talking to each other, for example, and they unwittingly move a little farther apart. The cameraman cannot hold both of them in his shot, and yet he cannot settle on one person and exclude the other. Then he must try to curb any artistic annoyance he feels, and attempt to include as much as possible of both people in his shot. Not very satisfactory —but what else can he do?

In fact, zoom lenses are so useful that cameramen must wonder how they ever manged without them.

Range of Focal Lengths

Nowadays zoom lenses with a ratio between maximum and minimum focal lengths of 10:1 are commonplace on OB units. Some are even equipped with 16:1 zoom lenses, an unheard-of luxury a few years ago. And with modern refinements such as servo and powered zoom mechanisms, shot boxes, high-speed zoom facilities and adaptors, the OB cameraman today is a lucky man.

And why not! As we know, much of the success of many types of OB depend on the skill of the cameraman, and these new lenses broaden the opportunities for good camerawork. Developments in zoom lens design have resulted in increased ranges, and marked improvements in picture quality. A 20:1 range is now available.

But for many years the standard ratio of 5:1 was the best the cameraman could expect from his zoom lens. This usually gave the cameraman a focal range of 4 in. to 20 in. or 8 in. to 40 in.

But there are certain limitations with these ranges. Let us look at the zoom lens with a range of 4 in. to 20 in. focal lengths. On the occasions when we can take a satisfactory long shot of a scene with the lens zoomed out to its 4-in. position, the zoomed-in, 20-in. position often proves to be inadequate if we want a tight close-up of part of that scene.

This might sound like a dangerous generalization, but it is often the case in practice. If a cameraman finds that he can frame an interesting long shot of a horse-race track, for example, with this lens in its zoomed-out position, he will be unable to frame a full-length shot of only one horse, unless it is no farther than about 200 ft. from his camera.

Dual-Range Lenses

On the other hand, although he can take close-ups of distant objects with an 8 in. to 40 in. zoom lens, the zoomed-out position will not normally be wide enough for long shots.

A zoom lens with a range of focal lengths from 4 in. to 40 in. (a ratio of 10:1) was needed for OB work. But there were no zoom lenses with that range available. In attempting to answer this need manufacturers designed an interesting compromise. This was a zoom lens having two ranges—4 in. to 20 in., and 8 in. to 40 in.—with provision for the cameraman to switch from one range to another in an instant.

If the action on the screen was so important that the niceties of camerawork could be overlooked, the ranges could even be changed while the camera was on the air. The picture would become diffused for an instant, and then clear as the new range was selected.

But even if these changes of range were confined to the occasions when the camera was not on the air, this zoom lens increased the versatility of the camera, and was far superior to other lenses on the market.

As we saw in the chapter on basic optics, the transmission factor for a zoom lens is relatively low—that is, a smaller amount of light will emerge than originally entered the lens.

Further, some zoom lenses cannot be "opened up" to more than about $f6.3$—a few have a maximum aperture of $f8$ only—and it follows that they cannot be used when the general light level is low. Most daylight OBs do not present many problems in this respect, but it is a point which must be borne in mind when considering the advisability of using zoom lenses.

Long-Focus Lenses

Where zoom lenses are not available, and close-ups are needed on distant objects, cameramen fit very long focal length lenses to their cameras. These normally range from about 12 in. to 40 in. focal length, and are mounted on the turret in the normal way.

The 40 in. lens, however, is often a very bulky piece of equipment, and some types take up as much room on a turret as a zoom lens. More often than not, no other lenses are mounted on the turret when the 40 in. lens is fitted—and with some equipment there is no opportunity to do otherwise.

This places a big restriction on the versatility of the camera, and the director should consider very carefully whether the value of this lens outweighs the possible disadvantages.

Filters

Lens filters are regularly used in photography and film making, so we might understandably expect to encounter them in television.

In fact, they are not widely used in television; except perhaps as neutral density filters, holding back over-bright sunlight on OBs. Then the appropriate transmission factor will be selected to match the lens aperture in use. Colour filters are only occasionally used, in monochrome, to increase tonal contrast—to emphasize clouds, for instance. Shaded sky filters are not suitable for cameras that pan or tilt. Diffusion discs and similar filters are only used for special effects.

Mobile Camera

Some OB units have been equipped for many years with a light-weight mobile camera, called a "creepy peepy". This is a camera which transmits its pictures by radio (no cable needed) to a CCU and which can be held in the cameraman's hands. Its ancillary equipment is sometimes strapped to the cameraman's back, and sometimes shared between him and an engineer.

The advantages of this type of camera can be imagined. The cameraman can visit places with his camera that had previously been out of the question. In fact, providing there was sufficient light and a man could get there, any spot could be visited and shot. It is quite common now to see shots taken from helicopters, for example, but these could not be attempted until the introduction of the mobile camera.

The pictures from them are not always of very high quality, but this is regarded as a small disadvantage compared with their versatility.

Operating Techniques

The variety of the OB cameraman's work, and the vast difference between the problems of one programme and the next, make it difficult to generalize on any aspect of OB camerawork. On the other hand it is impossible to discuss each type of programme that the cameraman might meet, and then study the techniques which should be adopted in order to shoot the programme correctly.

231

And yet there is a right and wrong way to shoot certain events—particularly those of a sporting nature—and there are certain basic techniques which the aspiring OB cameraman must be made aware of.

It might be worth our while, then, to single out some events, and look at the problems they present to the cameraman. Perhaps the advice will hold good for many other types of programme not mentioned here, and enable the cameraman to acquire a technique which will help him to overcome the specialized problems of each new type of programme he encounters.

Sport is universal, and we shall be reasonably certain that we are talking about the sort of programmes that every OB cameraman will find himself working on sooner or later if we concentrate on these types of events.

The best advice that can be given to an OB cameraman is that he should never, whatever the temptations, allow himself to become interested *as a spectator* in the particular sporting event he is shooting. It is a great help to the director if his cameramen understand the sport they are shooting. How else can they follow the action in such a way that the devotee—glued to his set at home—is seeing exactly what he wants to see? The cameraman is often solely responsible for the interest value of his shots and must react almost instinctively to the nature of the action taking place; it is logical that he will be more successful in his efforts if he knows his subject.

Concentration

The cameraman's knowledge and interest can be a disadvantage unless he concentrates firmly on his main reason for being at the event—to follow the action with his camera, and *not* to enjoy himself. It can be a disadvantage because it can so easily rob the cameraman of one of his most important qualities—concentration.

This is not surmise, it is fact. It has happened so many times to inexperienced cameramen that it cannot be ignored.

Take a soccer match as an example. The winger dribbles up to the defender, side-steps him neatly, leaves another defender helpless on the floor and passes the ball quickly to the centre-forward—who scores a goal. All very exciting, and just what the fans love to see.

The cameraman will attempt to follow all this, panning quickly with the pass to the centre-forward, zooming out to include the goal posts as the player prepares to shoot, and then zooming in for a closer view of the goalkeeper's desperate, unsuccessful attempt to save a goal.

But a spectator at the match would probably react in a different manner. He can see things out of the corner of his eye, and he has the ability to concentrate on small areas in his field of view while still retaining an impression of what is happening elsewhere. In the above example, he might allow his interest to dwell for a split second or two on the satisfying sight of the two bemused defenders before switching his concentration to the centre-forward in time to enjoy the exciting climax to the action.

To revert to the cameraman. If he is a soccer fan he might easily be similarly carried away by the action before him. He might just as easily react as a spectator, and hold his shot of the helpless defenders for part of a second longer than he should have done. But in that instant the ball will have left his frame. By the time he reacts to this and pans to the centre-forward, the ball might be in the back of the net.

That is not exaggeration; events really do move as quickly as that. And by relaxing his concentration for a split second, the cameraman can be responsible for marring what might well be the most exciting moment in the programme. He must remember that the viewer at home can see only what the cameraman shows him. He can see nothing out of the corner of his eye, and he is not interested in looking at two men lying on the floor while his team scores a goal just out of shot.

It is always possible to tell if a cameraman has been concentrating on his camerawork during events such as these. At the end of the programme he will remove his earphones and ask what the score was, or who won, or if it was an exciting event.

The cameraman must treat the transmission of sporting events mainly as a technical exercise, and yet he must attempt to contribute to the success of the programme by applying his knowledge of the particular sport to his technique.

The ball is kicked out of the top of frame, and the cameraman must continue panning to the spot where it will re-enter his shot. The cameraman who understands football will have no difficulty in picking the area of the field where the ball will land. He can tell by the players' reactions.

Meeting the Viewer's Need

That is a simple example of how knowledge of the sport can help the cameraman to contribute to the success of the programme. Yet the cameraman who is ignorant on sporting matters could easily have come to the same conclusion by intelligent reasoning.

233

What aspect of the action is the viewer interested in? Does he want to see the next bend included in the shot of the racing car? Does he want to see the player the ball will be passed to, or the fence the horse will jump, or the tape that the runner is striving to reach?

These are the sort of questions the cameraman should continually ask himself while covering sporting events. It is not sufficient to place the main subject—the ball, the racing car, the horse, or whatever it might be—in the centre of the frame, and then assume that the viewer will be satisfied. More thought than this must be applied to the technique of covering each individual type of event.

Let us take show jumping as an example. The camera pans around the course with the horse and rider—nothing could of simpler it would seem. The viewer will probably not be conscious that any special technique is called for.

But the cameraman will not place the rider in the centre be frame and then pan him around the course, keeping him in the same position in the shot throughout. As the rider approaches the obstacle, the cameraman will pan ahead a little to show the obstacle which the contestant is approaching. He will then pan the rider to the fence, and hold this in the centre of frame as the jump is made. When the horse lands the cameraman will not pan with it immediately. Instead he will delay his pan for an instant to allow the viewer to see whether or not the fence is still intact. Then, just before the rider nears the edge of the frame, he will pan in the direction of the movement, centring the rider for a while, then panning ahead of him for the next jump.

These variations in framing and uneven pans, however, will be unobtrusive—incredible though it may seem. They will be unobtrusive because the cameraman will have shown the viewer exactly what he wanted to see at every stage of the action taking place.

Of course these movements of the camera must not be as definite as the description of them might imply. They must flow into one another in a most subtle manner.

We have looked at an example of the technique needed for one aspect of a particular sport. It should not take much effort on the part of the cameraman to imagine how a similar technique can be applied to other sports. And it will involve no more effort for him to ask himself how he would cover certain events before he is called upon to do so.

234

He can learn much by studying other cameramen's techniques. An afternoon spent watching sporting events on his home receiver will be more value to him than a thousand words here. Even bad technique has its uses to the intelligent cameraman. If he can see what is wrong he is half-way to knowing how it should be done.

In fact cameramen should be quite certain in their own minds, before the programme is transmitted, exactly how they will present their shots to the best advantage. Half-way through a programme is not the time for the cameraman to discover that he has been using the wrong technique.

We have not discussed focusing. There is little need to, since the cameraman who works on an OB will be only too aware of the problems sooner or later! There is little depth of field available on a 40 in. lens—even at great distances. On many occasions the OB cameraman will have more focusing problems during a programme than his counterpart in the studio.

If he remembers the advice given in an earlier chapter he should be able to master them. It is something he must solve for himself, however, and this applies to everything he might have read in this book. He must experiment with the techniques described. He must practise them until they are second nature to him. No one can become a television cameraman—or anything else for that matter —merely by reading a book.

TECHNICAL TERMS

This glossary consists basically of terms used in British television. Equivalent American terms are denoted by an asterisk (*).

A APERTURE. The diameter of the iris opening of a lens—referred to by an *f*-number.

ARM SWINGER (*DOLLY PUSHER). The name normally given to the tracker who is responsible for controlling the pivoted arm of such dollies as cranes.

ARTIST. The designation given to anyone who appears in front of the television camera.

ASPECT RATIO. The ratio between the horizontal and vertical lengths of the picture frame. In television this is invariably 4 : 3.

B BACK PROJECTION (*REAR SCREEN PROJECTION). A method of projecting transparencies or cine film on to a screen, placed behind artists, to represent a still or moving background.

BARN DOOR. Metal projections attached to the front of a lamp and which can be set at a variety of positions to prevent the light from the lamp falling on specific areas in the set.

BURN. The phenomenon, common to some types of image orthicon tubes, in which a bright or high contrast image is more or less permanently imprinted on the photo cathode of the tube.

BOOM. The apparatus used by a member of the sound department to enable him to follow with a microphone the movements of artists.

C CAMERA ANGLE. The angle the camera makes with the subject it is shooting—regarded in a vertical as well as a horizontal sense, e.g. acute angle, high angle, etc.

CAMERA CONTROL UNIT (*VIDEO CONSOLE). The electronic apparatus supplying voltages and waveforms to the camera, and processing the resultant video signal (picture).

CANTED SHOT. A shot in which the subjects of the picture are made to appear tilted.

CAPPING UP. The procedure of masking the camera tube from any light which might fall on it.

CAPTION (*TITLE CARD). The card on which programme titles, production credits, etc. are normally drawn. The term is often applied to mounted photographs, maps, cartoons, etc. placed in front of the camera.

COMPOSITION. The art of arranging the elements of a scene in order to provide a pleasing, balanced, artistic picture, influencing mood, directing attention.

236

CRABBING. Movement of the camera across a scene and parallel to it.

CRANING. The raising of the camera by means of a pivoted arm as distinct from raising the camera vertically.

CRIB CARD (*SHOT LIST). The card on which are recorded the shots each cameraman must take during a programme. Also called "camera card".

CUE LIGHTS. The lights on the camera which—when lit—indicate that the vision mixer (or *technical director) has "cut" to that camera.

CUT (to). To switch to a picture emanating from another camera.

D DEFOCUSING. Causing a picture to be out of focus.

DEFOCUS MIX. A method of transition from one shot to another. The first picture is defocused and then mixed through to a defocused picture on another camera. This picture is then brought into focus after the mix has been completed.

DEPTH OF FIELD. The difference between the nearest and furthest distances a subject can be placed from a lens in order to remain acceptably in focus.

DIFFERENTIAL FOCUSING. The method of arranging a shot so that the subject stands out in sharp relief against an out-of-focus backing.

DISSOLVING. See MIXING.

DOLLY. Any kind of camera mounting which can be moved around the studio. Also used as a verb, meaning to move the camera mounting.

*DOLLY PUSHER. See ARM SWINGER.

F F-NUMBER (stop, aperture). The number marked on the "iris ring" of a lens to indicate the aperture at which it is set.

FILTER. A transparent material placed between the lens and the tube in order to regulate the light intake, modify tonal values, image clarity, etc.

FILTER WHEEL. A disc, holding the filters, which can be rotated between the lens and the tube to provide prompt insertion of filters when required. This wheel often incorporates the capping device for the camera.

FLARING (Lens flare). The halo-like effect of a bright light striking the lens.

FLOODING. Operating the controls of a lamp to provide a wide beam of light.

FOOTROOM. The distance between an artist's feet and the bottom of the cameraman's picture.

FRAME. The term usually given to the edges of the television picture.

FRENCH FLAG. A metal plate, having an extendable arm, placed in front of a lamp to prevent light falling on certain areas in a set.

H HEADROOM. The distance between an artist's head and the top of the cameraman's picture.

I INCIDENT RAY. A ray of light falling on to a surface.

IRIS. The control on the lens which maintains a circular aperture when opened or closed to govern the light intake.

J JELLY (Wire, *Scrim). A wire mesh suspended in a gelatine compound which can be inserted in front of a lamp to reduce the intensity of the light emanating from it.

JIBBING (*TONGUING). Horizontal movement of a camera by means of a pivoted arm, as distinct from crabbing.

237

K   KEYSTONING. The apparent converging of vertical lines caused by the camera not being at right angles to these lines.

L   LENS HOOD. A tubular accessory or shield attached to a lens to prevent extraneous light falling on to it and creating lens flares.

LOOKING ROOM. The space allowed between an artist's face and the edge of frame when the artist is not facing the camera.

M   MATCHING. The procedure carried out by the vision control operator (or *video engineer) to equate the quality of the television picture emanating from two or more cameras.

MINIMUM FOCUSING DISTANCE. The smallest distance a subject can be placed from a lens and still remain in focus.

MIXING (Dissolving). Simultaneously fading out one picture while fading up another, so that one appears to dissolve into the other.

MONITOR. A television set, used in a studio, which can be supplied with any one of many sources.

O   OPENING UP. The process of increasing the diameter of the iris of a lens in order to admit more light.

P   PANNING. Horizontal rotation of a camera about a static base. Derived from the word "panorama".

PANNING HANDLE. The handle (attached to the panning head) which is held by the cameraman and which gives him greater control over camera movement.

PANNING HEAD (Pan-and-tilt head). The item of equipment to which the camera is attached and which enables smooth, stable camera movement to be accomplished. The head itself is firmly attached to the camera mounting by bolts or locking rings.

PERSPECTIVE. The illusion of depth created by the disposition of line, tone and mass in a picture, together with the judicious use of lenses and camera positions.

PIVOTING. The practice of hinging about one or more of the edges of a picture during camera movement in order to provide an unobtrusive and logical transition from one type of shot to another.

PLOPPING FOCUS (Throwing focus). A fast movement of the focusing mechanism in order to switch the point of focus in a picture from one subject to another.

PROPS. The name commonly given to those articles which are used to embellish a set. Derived from properties.

R   *REAR SCREEN PROJECTION (R.P.) see BACK PROJECTION.

REFOCUSING. Bringing into focus a picture that is out of focus (soft).

REMBRANDT LIGHTING. A lighting arrangement in which the key light is placed at an angle of 45 degrees (horizontally) to the subject.

S   *SCRIM. See JELLY.

SCRIPT. The written "blue print" of a television programme. It will contain every point of artistic and technical detail necessary to its production.

SET. Any arrangement of pieces of scenery, articles of furniture, drapes, floor designs, etc. to create a recognisable area which will supplement the artists in a television programme.

SET DRESSINGS. The additions to a set which enhance it artistically, or which add to its realism and/or authenticity.

SHOT. An uninterrupted picture from one camera.

*SHOT LIST. See CRIB CARD.

SOFT. The term used to describe a picture that is not sharply focused.

SPLITTING FOCUS. Focussing the lens somewhere between two or more subjects in order to include them in the depth of field. This is done when focusing sharply on one subject would cause the other/s to be out of focus.

SPOTTING. The practice of directing the light emanating from a lamp along a sharply defined beam (opposite to flooding q.v.)

STICKING. See BURN.

STOPPING DOWN. Reducing the diameter of the iris in order to admit less light through a lens.

T   TAKING POSITION. The position on a lens turret which is in line with the camera tube. Any lens placed at this point is said to be in the taking position.

*TECHNICAL DIRECTOR. See VISION MIXER.

THROWING FOCUS. See PLOPPING FOCUS.

*TITLE CARD. See CAPTION.

TILTING. Vertical rotation of a camera about a static base.

TONGUING. See GIBBING.

TRACKER. A camera assistant responsible for movement of a camera mounting.

TRACKING (*TRUCKING, *DOLLYING). Movement of a camera towards or away from a subject.

TRANSMISSION. The period during which a television programme is "on the air".

TUBE CARRIAGE. The moveable cradle which holds the camera tube in place in the camera.

TURRET. That part of the camera to which the lenses are attached. It can be rotated to enable any lens to be placed in the taking position with a minimum of delay.

V   *VIDEO CONSOLE. See CAMERA CONTROL UNIT.

*VIDEO ENGINEER. See VISION CONTROL OPERATOR.

VIEWFINDER. The miniature television monitor, incorporated in a camera, which displays the picture emanating from that camera only.

VIEWFINDER HOOD. The hooded projection attached to a viewfinder to prevent unwanted light from degrading the viewfinder picture.

VISION CONTROL OPERATOR (*Video engineer). The technician controlling picture quality by operating exposure, sit, colour balance, etc.

VISION MIXER (*TECHNICAL DIRECTOR). The person responsible for the operation of the vision mixing panel. This panel is also frequently called a "vision mixer".

W   WHIP PAN (*WIZZ PAN, *SWISH PAN, *ZIP PAN). A very rapid pan from one subject to another during which all detail on the screen becomes blurred by the speed of the camera movement. Normally used when a "shock effect" is required.

WIRE. See JELLY.

Z   ZOOM LENS. A lens having multiple, moveable elements and providing a variable focal length. Operating the controls of this lens produces the effect of moving into or out from a scene—hence zooming in and zooming out.

INDEX